From the Hand of Man

Resources for the Study of Anthropology

Edited by
James A. Clifton

From the Hand of Man

Primitive and Preindustrial Technologies

Robert F. G. Spier

Houghton Mifflin Company · Boston
New York · Atlanta · Geneva, Illinois · Dallas · Palo Alto

Printed in the U.S.A.

To Leslie Spier
Who was personally and professionally
Responsible for this venture

Contents

Foreword

In an age when rapidly accelerating technologies promise to make modern man a mere caretaker of the incomprehensibly complex machines he has created, a fresh anthropological assessment of the beginnings and growth of the means by which man has controlled and modified his environment should help place the technological present and future in perspective. It was the invention of techniques for extending the reach, increasing strength, and enriching the skills of the organism which made man of proto-men and which then contributed immeasurably to his development and variety. In this rich and insightful book Professor Spier examines and evaluates some of the varieties of specific technologies created by man for attaining desirable technical ends. He examines the growth and functions of these technologies but does not isolate his inquiry to make technology a closed and static system. Instead, he places technology in a richer perspective — conjoined with facets of social organization, connected to symbolism and the arts, and analyzed in terms of human creativity and adaptation. All the illustrations are the author's original work, drawn from his life-long involvement in the study of cultural things.

JAMES A. CLIFTON

Acknowledgments

I wish to acknowledge my indebtedness to the many people who were partially involved in the creation of this book. Stimuli came from many directions: first, from some of my teachers — most directly J. O. Brew and the late Lauristan Ward, both of whom administered a legacy from R. B. Dixon; second, the constant proddings and additions from students, among them J. R. Vincent and Charles and Bonnie Keller; third, the encouragement to form a course on the subject of preindustrial technologies which came from D. A. Baerreis; and fourth, the wisdom and counsel of colleagues, including D. R. Henning, John H. Rowe, Michael J. Harner, and H. C. Wilson. A specific contribution was made by A. H. Gayton who read a large portion of the manuscript and made valuable amendations. James A. Clifton has played his role as Series Editor in good style — having been encouraging, patient, and critical in the right proportions. There are many others who have participated both directly and indirectly in the development of this book, not the least of these being the members of my immediate family, who have respected the needs of authorship. I thank them all.

1

Introduction

The term technology may be broadly or narrowly used. In the broadest sense, it may refer to all the technical activities of men in all times and places. Only occasionally does one's view possess such scope. More narrowly, a group's technology may include all its own technical activities but not those of another time nor those of other groups. Most narrowly, technology may refer to a series of coordinated activities about some central subject or core. So one may refer, with ever-increasing specificity, to human technology, to twentieth-century Western (Euro-American) technology, or to the textile technology of contemporary Guatemala.

Each technology, whether broadly or narrowly conceived, may be seen to consist of a series of coordinated techniques or particular methods of reaching a technical goal — the molding of pottery, the carding of wool, or the tempering of metal. Though technologies in the narrower senses are usually distinct, their techniques may be shared by several technologies. Burnishing, for example, may smooth the surface of a pot as well as that of a metal piece. Casting is likewise a shared technique found in both ceramics and metallurgy. However, similarity of name should not be the basis for judgment of technical sharing, as the process of tempering clay for ceramics cannot be equated with tempering in metallurgy.

"Technology" is used in this study to refer to the means by which man seeks to modify or control his natural environment. Excluded are the magico-religious means by which he may seek the same ends. It is tempting to confine technology to "rational" means, but this is best avoided when we are unable to examine others' rationalities. It should be noted here that technological pursuits may have their magico-religious aspects, but these are auxiliary to an avowedly technical approach.

In the same way as magico-religious activities are excluded, somewhat arbitrarily, from technology by our definition, so also are social techniques. These also may be viewed as means to an end: the control or alteration of the environment (primarily social). Though neither social elements nor magico-religious elements can be ignored, they are not central to our business. They will, however, be introduced at appropriate points for they both have their relevance to technological concerns.

In this discussion of man's technological activities, the emphasis will be on phenomena occurring among primitive peoples. (Call them preliterate, nonliterate, preindustrial, nonindustrial, or non-Western, if you wish.) There are three major reasons for this interest. First, the history of technology reaches almost without a break from the crude pebble tools of the African Australopithecines to the most complex, computer-controlled devices of today. One cannot properly understand modern technology without some knowledge of its antecedents. Though the record is less complete for the remote past than for more recent times, the archeologist's researches have provided a general outline. Surprisingly, the recent record is not complete, for historians of all ages have tended to overlook the prosaic activities of technicians. There are some notable exceptions to this generality, but they are altogether too rare.

Second, concentration on the simpler technologies makes possible a better grasp of basic technical processes. If the analogy may be permitted, one starts his study of biology with simpler organisms, not with the most complex ones known. In the same way, a look at the simpler technologies helps us avoid being overwhelmed by the more complex ones. The basic steps with which we are concerned are usually separate in the simpler technologies and readily discerned; the goals and end products are well within our comprehension.

The third reason lies in our own history and that of the rest of the world. Most aspects of technology discussed here were a part of our immediate past. Many of these continue, substantially unchanged, into the present of some societies. The Industrial Revolution, which so drastically changed our lives, has occurred during the past two centuries. It did not alter all of our technological world at the same rate or at the same time. There remain today, even in the Western world, pockets of practices which are little altered from the Middle Ages or earlier. Indeed, many groups have been little touched by the Industrial Revolution and remain in a technological state not far different from that of the preindustrial Western world. If one is to understand much of the modern world, this understanding will be enhanced by knowledge of the various technologies of the people living in it.

Technological Input

A technological pursuit requires an input so that a situation may be created, procedures followed, and a result obtained. The three major elements of the technological input are knowledge, resources, and labor.

A group's knowledge has a great bearing on its technological capability and behavior. Though innovation occurs, action stemming from innovation constitutes a small part of the behavior at any given time. Most technical knowledge is a legacy from earlier times. It is only in periods of great innovative activity that any substantial portion of the effective knowledge of a generation is new. Estimates have been made of the continuing elements, the legacy, in some limited technological spheres (Kroeber, 1948:263). Despite their rather impressionistic character, the estimates tend to confirm the essential continuity involved. They also indirectly support the notion that people rarely rise above the general level of technical knowledge of their time. What is known at a given moment is, then, a strong limiting factor in technological behavior. However, pure knowledge, that of science, frequently runs well in advance of practical knowledge, that of technology. The lag, which always exists to some degree, is variable. It is influenced by the rate of scientific advance, the ease of communication between science and technology, and the state of the society.

Resources constitute the second element of the technological input. Their availability and the knowledge to exploit them are factors in the end result of technological activity. If the resources are not present locally, a society imports them (at what cost?) or does without. However, the presence of resources is no guarantee of their utilization. The group may lack the knowledge prerequisite to exploitation or it may, for some reason, decide not to use them. Taboos on places, plants, or animals may prevent their use despite their presence. The absence or scarceness of certain resources may either inhibit some lines of technological development or may, less commonly, call forth remarkable ingenuity in the use of substitutes or the economical use of a scant supply. Whatever the circumstances, there is rarely a *direct* correlation between the presence of resources and their utilization.

Labor, like the other elements of input, is subject to many ancillary considerations. Both quantity and quality of labor have their importance.

As to the former, some undertakings are difficult or impossible if the manpower is not available or cannot be organized toward the task. The disclosure, through archeological investigation, of large public works is usually taken as prima facie evidence of some social complexity. However, a simple census could not reveal the labor force applicable in a given situation. Many of those present may not work toward the stated goal for social or even ritual reasons. Conversely, the society may be able to call on the labor of those not normally in its work force when an exceptional task is at hand. One must remember, additionally, that even in the simplest societies there is often a sharp division between the work of men and women which precludes any of the one sex engaging in the work of the other. Finally, problems of labor availability may call forth ingenious solutions to technological problems. It has been noted that frontier areas may suffer from a labor shortage and often deal with this problem by the employment of labor-saving devices and labor-saving techniques. Among the latter may be counted the practice of dispensing with some of the niceties of life which characterize more settled areas — a practice which often gives the frontier its rawness and roughness.

Technological Output

The output of technological activities is twofold: material culture and environmental modifications. It is, within our definition, the avowed purpose of technology to modify and control the natural environment.

Material culture is the name given to the man-made physical products of human behavior patterns, including structures, clothing, other containers: the whole paraphernalia with which man surrounds himself. This is the stuff which builds tells and middens, the hunting grounds of the archeologist.

The bulk of this output is certainly in the category of consumer goods, but it may be a measure of technological sophistication when some production is directed back into the technologies themselves to increase their ultimate efficiency. Though the earliest hominids are known primarily through their tools, this may be a consequence of conditions of preservation rather than a true reflection of their technological output. In later times, with a better archeological record, the tool inventory remains fairly stable while other artifacts increase in numbers. Quite recently with the Industrial Revolution a change has diverted a substantial part of production into other than consumer goods channels. However intriguing and thought provoking such a yardstick of technological advancement may be, it is one which would be difficult to apply.

Environmental modifications are another aspect of the technological output. From the individual's standpoint, some of this modification comes in housing, clothing, heating, cooling, and so forth. Another part of the modification comes through the development of routes of communication — roads, bridges, tunnels. Other artifacts which are prominent on the landscape are dams, irrigation and drainage canals, artificial (and artificially augmented) harbors, land "made" through the filling of marshes and watercourses, and similar large engineering works.

However, environmental modifications resulting from man's activities are not always so obvious. Deforestation has had major effects in Europe and China. The cultivation of virgin soils, as on the Great Plains of the United States, has also had its consequences in erosion. For millenia the land-clearing activities of slash-and-burn (swidden, milpa) cultivators have changed the character of vegetation in tropical and subtropical areas. While one should not underestimate the past effects of human technologies, it is in more recent times that these have become intensified. Various types of mining, for example, hydraulic and strip mining, have disturbed large areas of land. Other types of mining have left their spoil piles and mill tailings in evidence. The burning of hydrocarbon fuels has created radical changes in the atmosphere, locally if not generally. Some authorities feel that the added carbon compounds in the air have resulted in the warming of the entire world climate. Finally, the growth and concentration of population, along with growing industrial wastes, have altered the nature of many streams and possibly the oceans.

While man has always left his mark on the land (no doubt to the gratification of the archeologists), it is apparent that he is doing so increasingly. The growing world population without any parallel increase in the land available and the growth of technological capacity have increased the intensity of exploitation of natural resources and quantity of waste products. It has even been suggested that ultimately man may become extinct through the fouling of his own nest.

2

Technology and Culture

The technological abilities of man are a part of his culture and are learned and transmitted outside the genetic realm. Though it may be argued that nest building or similar activities of other animals are also learned (at least in part), the differences in both the quantity and quality of man's cultural activities from animal homologues are sufficient to elevate those of man to another level. The argument is an old one, and this is not the place to attempt a settlement.

The significance of the cultural character of technology is far-reaching since technologies are more or less integrated with all other aspects of culture — religious activities, political activities, economic activities, everything which man does, however categorized. The degree and the nature of that integration is not the same, of course, in all areas of culture. Neither is the balance ever any more than momentary. We are dealing with a dynamic situation. However, any activity which uses or controls material objects is linked to some technology through those objects. Even those activities which are substantially mental — philosophies, oral literature — have their connections. The views which participants in a culture hold about worldly possessions, creature comforts, manual labor, and man's integration with the natural world all have some bearing on technological activities. Bear in mind that these relationships run in both directions. For example, technology has an influence on philosophy and, in its turn, philosophy has an influence on technology.

The integration of technology within culture will become increasingly apparent as we continue, but some examples presented at this time might make the reader more aware of this relationship.

Connections with the political structure are found in many areas of communications technology: in the location, construction, and maintenance of road nets; in subsidies for railroads, airlines, and shipping; in the size of political administrative units (which have expanded as travel has been facilitated); and in the control of traffic. Additionally, political bodies have allocated scarce resources (whether helium in the United States or trees suitable for canoe building in aboriginal Polynesia) and encouraged technological innovations through patents, prizes, and monopolies.

Social structure and technologies are similarly related. The social standing of workers and technicians, especially as these come to be a special segment of the society through the development of so-called true division of labor, may either encourage or inhibit technological pursuits. In earlier times, and to a lesser degree today, technical knowledge and technical facilities were transmitted in family lines or within some larger kinship unit such as the caste. The recruitment of technicians, even in the absence of direct inheritance, often lay within a group of kinsmen. Social status in many societies is correlated with the ability to command, accumulate, and distribute material goods. It has been suggested that a sociopolitical structure, the ramage in central Polynesia, was the product of the distribution and means of exploitation of scattered natural resources. Self-sufficiency in resources would have been associated with a different organization (Sahlins, 1958).

Though the bond is not as evident, religion and technology are also linked. At various times and places, as in dynastic Egypt and medieval Europe, a large proportion of the technological output has been directed toward religious concerns. Pyramids and cathedrals are the tangible fruits of these enterprises. Less obvious are the techniques and other advances which resulted from the pressures of the times. Most of these were applicable to other pursuits. In addition, religious ritual has been practiced to insure the success of various technologies. Without proper care for the supernatural world, the efforts of man were likely to fail or fall short of complete success.

The economic world is engaged with the products of technologies or the labor which goes into their production. The relationship here is probably the most obvious and accepted of all those we have discussed; however, there are some subtleties involved. The form of the economy —

whether by barter or cash, by market or not — may encourage or deter specialization to supply products to a wide trade area. If a community is limited in its trade perspectives, then specializations will be few and mild in effect.

Because technology is a part of culture, there may be applied to it all of the concepts which deal with culture generally. These may be used, perhaps more than they have been in the past, in the analysis of technology. All the elements of theories of cultural dynamics are applicable, among them cultural evolution in its various forms, diffusion and its adjuncts, and functionalism of various persuasions. However, this statement is more an article of faith than an exposition of the approaches actually used. Some have yet to be applied to technological analysis.

The discussion above has stressed the integration of technology with the rest of culture, a circumstance that few would deny. There is another relationship which is urged by some writers who maintain that technology determines the state of the rest of the culture. Put another way, technology is the independent variable and other cultural aspects are dependent variables. This contention is particularly plausible and seductive in our technologically-oriented modern world. When we seem to have better control over our technological life than over our social or political life, it is comforting to believe that through the one we really are directing the others.

Outstanding among the technological determinists of anthropological persuasion is Leslie A. White who has developed an abstract theory of general evolution which traces the development of human culture through the ages. According to White, the technology of a society is responsible for its social organization which, in turn, is responsible for its ideology. The emphasis is upon the group's physical survival through development and maintenance of a system for environmental exploitation, that is, an effective adaptation. The social order is supportive of the exploitational scheme, and the ideological order provides a rationale, after the fact, for the whole system of behavior. There is general agreement among anthropologists on the mutually supportive relationship of these aspects of man's existence. They agree that the social order is functionally related to the subsistence economy and that the ideological order provides a justification for both. The differences in outlook, if any, arise as a result of the point at which one starts. White is quite certain that the origination of the complex of relationships lies in the technological order. He builds from there forward, not back toward that aspect from social or ideological order, nor in a series of loops (White, 1949, 1959).

White believes also that one may measure man's progress through the ages in terms of the amount of power available to him. When man started as an Australopithecine, he had only the power of his own body.

Today, millions of years later, he can command the power of the atomic nucleus. At points in between he has added to his own power that of domestic animals, water, wind, and fossil fuels. The sources of power have proliferated, and the amount of available power is now impressive. The problems with White's approach lie in the times at which additions were made and with the measurement of the results.

For ninety-nine percent of man's existence he had no power beyond that of his body. The only reasonable exception to this statement would involve the uses which he made of fire. These are difficult to surmise and even more difficult to convert into quantitative terms. He may have saved his energy or expanded his capabilities by hunting animals with fire drives. He may have reduced the effort of stone chipping by heating the stone beforehand. How can one tell what the gain was in each of these practices? Since those early times we note the addition of draft animals, water wheels, windmills, steam engines, and internal combustion engines. While we have good estimates of the power developed in recent centuries and can convert these figures into measures on a per capita basis, for earlier times we cannot do as much.

In essence, the quantitative evaluation of progress in terms of harnessed power is theoretically acceptable. It may be possible to make and use such evaluations for modern nations or within the recent historic period. However, the customary anthropological perspective has a longer focus than this, and the evaluative technique loses much force at a distance. It becomes, like many of White's theoretical positions, one which is generally true but not specifically applicable.

Aside from any questions of theoretical orientation, we find that the technological side of man's existence is a part of his culture. The behavior which we so categorize is not random or extemporized but stimulated and guided by ideas and experiences shared by members of a social group. In this respect, technology is cultural.

Technology and Environment

The technological aspect of culture is responsive to the same natural environment which it seeks to control. The relationship is clearly bi-directional — the environment sets the problems which the technology must master while simultaneously furnishing the resources for its own potential subjugation.

Environmental determinism, which considered culture to be a product of its environment, was common in the nineteenth century and persisted into the twentieth. (See Ratzel and Huntington as examples.) Geographers have come to view the relationship in a slightly different perspective, but many other scholars continue to hold such a deterministic view.

The natural environment is more properly seen as permissive or limiting in its effects on culture. The choice between these two words depends more on the viewer's focus than on the nature of the relationship. One may stress the variety of adaptations which cultures make within a given environment. Or, one may stress that some or many adaptations are prohibited by environmental limitations.

At any point in history a culture is equipped with a certain stock of knowledge or belief which underlies and motivates its practices. The technological part of this stock has two sources: one innovative, the other diffusionary. The innovative segment, discovered or invented by members of the society, has developed within the culture. Being of local origin, it will be more closely related to the environmental circumstances than will the diffusionary segment which comes from outside the culture, that is, from other cultures in other places. The biological needs of man, as related to environmental problems (of drought, heat, cold, forestation, and so forth), may be expected to channel innovative thoughts in certain directions. Only in this sense can the environment be called determinative. The elements transmitted in diffusionary contacts were developed elsewhere, in another environment. They must, of course, be able to be related to the environment and culture into which they are diffusing, but they cannot be held to have been generated in that context.

The behavior of a given people within an environment, as seen through their cultural practices, is a product of what they happen to know at the time. A new technique or outlook, developed locally or diffused from outside the culture, may send activities in an entirely new direction. The introduction of food cultivation to a previously foraging people occurs without immediate environmental change, but the people's relation to the environment has been altered.

Yet, in setting aside a deterministic view as erroneous, one must acknowledge that the alternatives which remain are not clear-cut. The permissive position recognizes a range of adaptation which is not absolute, but is linked quite closely to the state of the culture. A broad technological spectrum may open possibilities which would remain closed to societies with limited technical resources. For example, a group dependent upon woody fuels might find life extremely difficult in contrast to a society which knew how to utilize fossil fuels (coal and petroleum) present in the environment. Similarly, a culture which includes substantial transport capabilities is able to move food, fuel, and other necessities from place to place to create a comfortable life. This may be begging the question, however, for the importation of these stuffs means either that the environment has been altered, or that a larger environmental sphere is actually being exploited — whichever way you care to view it. But, with regard to the focus of this discussion, the cultural capability has altered the situation and the environment now permits, so to speak, this adaptation along with any others which may have been present.

Seeing the environment as limiting in its effects produces a similar result: the environment limits the range of adaptive types through prohibition of other adaptive types. Modern man has faith in his ability to solve all environmental problems in time and finds it difficult to accept the idea of an environment which prohibits any kind of cultural form. This view is found in the motto — "the difficult we do immediately, the impossible takes a little longer" — this is not as facetious as it first appears.

Regardless of one's faith in the ultimate triumph of technology, there remains the question of practicality. It is easier for the simpler culture than for a complex one to maintain itself in a rigorous environment. This statement must not be misinterpreted and demands immediate elaboration. The contrast of simple and complex suggests a difference in "bulk" and the interconnections between the parts of the culture. Complexity is not equated here with technological sophistication. The use of atomic reactors as energy sources in the Arctic is not to be confused with an attempt to transplant American suburbia to an Arctic environment. At some point along the line of increasing complexity of operations the law of diminishing returns sets in: the effort to possess and utilize all of the paraphernalia of modern life becomes too great for the returns received. Though the proper British traveler of the nineteenth century may have taken along his folding bathtub and dressed for dinner in the wilds, there was a much stronger tendency for Westerners to "go native" and strip their style of living to the essentials. In "going native" they approximated native cultural adaptations.

This discussion of the importation of culture into a region through colonization or exploration is pertinent also to the development of cultures entirely within the region. An impressive correlation exists between environmental rigor (in terms of cold, heat, aridity, and similar factors) and cultural simplicity. The exceptions — represented by the Eskimo, for example — are cases of technological sophistication rather than cultural complexity. Some cultures, under these circumstances, have produced ingenious, specialized devices and techniques, though they have not employed esoteric principles in their conception.

Regardless of the type and sources of environmental adaptation, it is clear that man lives within a "technological shield" which surrounds him with an artificial micro-environment. The relationship of man to environment is actually the relationship of two environments — the cultural and the natural. No man can be said truly to dwell in a totally natural environment. He will alter it in some way.

The technological shield protects man from the elements, from other animals, and from himself. Because of it he can warm himself, sleep soundly, produce basically helpless offspring, and eat an artificial diet. Through the millenia this artificial (i.e., cultural or technological) environment has had its effects on the physical nature of man himself.

Without dwelling on those circumstances which led to the transition from ape to proto-hominid to man, let us consider the factors which are deemed generally responsible for biological change in man as well as in the nonhuman living world — natural selection, mutation, population mixture, and genetic drift.

Natural selection includes the various pressures on slightly different forms of an organism such that one type survives and reproduces better than another. Darwin's "survival of the fittest" is a stark expression of these pressures. Natural selection refers not to immediate survival or extinction, but to relative rates of survival. This fact coupled with the general zoological proposition that only one organism may occupy a given ecological niche at a time means that those forms possessing certain advantageous features, vis-à-vis the environment, will ultimately survive, and the rest will not.

The advent of culture has altered the environment in which the selection occurs, though not the principle of selection. Perhaps now survival or greater efficiency goes with speed of nervous reaction, greater intellect, or the ability to conceal one's feelings. The stakes have not altered, but the game has. Because culture compensates the individual for those physical features which formerly were disadvantageous or even lethal, people are alive today to reproduce their own kind, who in earlier years would have perished from physical disability, vital insufficiency, or low resistance to disease. So the process of selection continues, but not like the natural selection of the past.

Mutation involves abrupt changes in genetic composition from parent to child such that the offspring possesses inheritable traits not present in either parent. The natural causes of mutations are a bit obscure, but we do know how to increase mutation rates, and we presume that some of the causes (radiation and chemical activity) may be natural ones. As culture grows more complex and makes increasing use of chemicals and radioactivity, we may expect an increased production of individuals with mutations. Many of these individuals now survive who would have been doomed in earlier times.

Population mixture increased recently with mass migrations and better transportation. However, if the facts were known, it is likely that the opportunity has increased more than its acceptance, for most people still marry amongst themselves; the factor of propinquity may carry the day.

Only genetic drift has not been altered noticeably by the changed circumstances of cultural life. The mischances and accidents which led to the loss of genetic materials must still occur. "Loss" in this context means a failure to perpetuate, as when a woman who bears the genes for color-blindness fails to have children. Genetic drift is most effective in small, isolated populations in which the gene pool is limited and any change will have maximum effects. However, the small, isolated populations which maximized the effects of genetic drift are now disappearing, and so genetic drift correspondingly may become far less important. Thus the modern circumstance, while not influencing the causes of drift, has greatly reduced its consequences.

This discussion has stressed the consequences of man's possession of culture for his biological side — an aspect, one might have supposed, hardly to be influenced by the technological shield. Beyond this one sees rather readily the components of the shield — shelter, food, social dictation of breeding choices, growing medical capabilities, and so on.

No man lives in the natural environment. Rather, each man lives in an environment which is largely the result of his own and his fellow's technological capabilities.

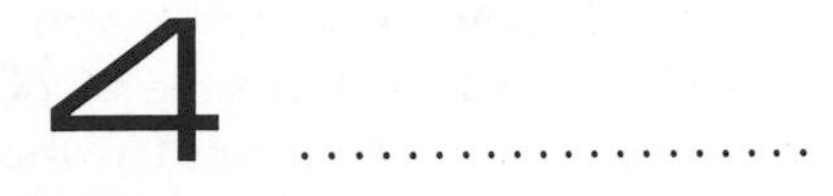

The Technological Complex

Technology is not composed solely of coordinated techniques. Many other elements, some considerably removed from technology, enter the picture. There are the obvious tools, materials, and personnel, as well as the less tangible motivations, designs, and standards, all of which make up the technological scene. Though the less tangible elements are more difficult to discern and evaluate than the former triad, they may not be ignored.

The elements listed above exist in a "Gestalt" relationship — as a totality, literally a form or figure, whose nature is such that the whole is greater than the simple sum of its parts. In other words, any technological situation must be viewed as a complex entity since a summation of its components, however fully identified, still falls short of the total.

The Gestaltist approach may be fruitful when one considers a technology from the viewpoint of its practitioners. The technologist faced with a particular task will, consciously or not, evaluate the situation in terms of materials, means, skills, personnel, time, costs, and standards of quality. In the decision process the technologist may ask himself, for example, if the task is likely to be sufficiently recurrent to warrant the time-consuming manufacture of special tools or fixtures which would save time in the long run if the task is to be repetitive. He may also ask if, in the interests of speed or economy he should lower customary standards of quality or use substitute materials. He may evaluate his own and other available skills as sufficient to meet the demands of time or of quality. Further estimations are usually made as the technologist works within his knowledge of the available resources and the expectations of the situation. Thorough understanding of these complex evaluative processes still awaits formal research, which may prove difficult to accomplish without recourse to introspection.

To clarify the nature of the elements in this complex and to explore their relationships within it, let us examine some of them in detail. The discussion of tools and materials will be postponed for examination later.

Technological personnel vary considerably in their origins, their involvement, and their training. In societies which lack a true division of labor (the specialization which usually accompanies food surpluses) work is usually parcelled out on the bases of age and sex. Further, technological activities, especially women's occupations, are usually pursued in the home when possible. While men engage in stoneworking, woodworking, and metalworking, women make pottery, weave textiles, tan leather, pursue needle-using tasks, and make baskets and mats. Children of both sexes may assist in women's work, but a segregation occurs as maturity is approached. In old age, again, individuals of both sexes may engage in women's occupations.

Full-time specialization, usually undertaken by men, may involve tasks which are traditionally assigned to women on a part-time basis. This may mean only that women cannot be excused from domestic duties and child-rearing to become full-time practitioners of their customary crafts. Alternatively, this difference at the full-time level may reflect the society's definition of its livelihood. Thus a man's activity as a full-time technician determines the source of his family's living.

Simple societies permit little choice within sex-differentiated activities, and everyone turns his hand to *all* tasks appropriate to his sex. Any variation from this rule is usually attributable to differences in skill. Insofar as his skill may fall short of the acceptable standard, the individual may do less than his normal share of that particular work. When skill rises above the norm, the reverse may be true, but not to the extent of full-time occupation, since simple societies are usually unable to support full-time involvement in one pursuit by any individual.

However, sex-differentiation may persist beyond the point in cultural elaboration at which full-time technical personnel appear. In such cases the craft may tend to follow family lines. Reinforcing this hereditary tendency are factors of familiarity, availability of instruction, admission to trade secrets, family control of resources, and market connections.

Most of these considerations flow from the nature of the situation. The family member responds to the suggestions or circumstances by following in the footsteps of the same-sexed parent. Other choices for occupational specialization are open but are not as convenient or appealing. The ultimate in occupational inheritance is found with the full-developed caste system in which each caste engages in a traditional occupation. The castes and occupations may be more or less finely divided, and the actual affiliation may be with a class of occupations or with a very specific one. As times and technologies have changed, a discrepancy has developed between the actual occupation of a caste and its ostensible one. Whether the relationship of caste and occupation be real or putative, it still exists as a social force which is applied to the individual from without the group; he has no choice but to follow the family occupation or another of the same type or class. In addition outsiders are prevented from entering a specific caste's occupation.

Under these circumstances training presents few problems. The novice learns by observing and then by assisting older practitioners in his family group who engage in these activities. Only when the technological pursuit is carried on away from home must an effort be made to observe and participate. Even here, when possible, children may accompany adults and assist them. Boys are more likely than girls to delay their introduction to adult activities because a higher percentage of general male activities (but not male technological activities) are conducted away from the dwelling area where smaller boys may not be able to observe them.

Though no systematic study of the subject is available, the training of novices by persons other than kinsmen seems rare among nonliterate peoples. Formal apprenticeship, similar to that known in Europe, is reported from Samoa where professionalism of technicians was unusually well developed (Handy, 1923:143). In a nonliterate society the chances of learning a craft not followed in one's family were generally low. We must remember, however, that families were often broadly defined and specialization was not highly developed. The only clear-cut barrier to alternative training was, again, where occupation followed caste lines.

Compensation to craftsmen is also linked to kinship and social organization. Among nonliterates the economic unit is the family, nuclear or extended. No individual, even if unmarried, works solely for himself. Rather, the returns of his labor, in cash or kind, are shared with close kin, and theirs with him. These reciprocal obligations and privileges provide a measure of security which may have repercussions in the technological order.

When a craftsman need not depend on immediate returns from his labor in order to eat, he is substantially freed from the press of time. Though progressing at a suitable pace, the worker may experiment with slow techniques, high standards, attention to detail, ornamentation beyond a simple level, and careful thought. The group's willingness to support the worker through a long production period with no returns makes possible certain results which would not otherwise be forthcoming. Because the group will ultimately share, directly or vicariously, in the economic and prestige rewards which follow, it has in essence capitalized the craftsman. If the group finds the support a burden it will probably make it evident to the worker. He, in turn, must expect to make a similar contribution to the capitalization of others when he is able.

Through the close links between kinship, residence, economy, and the operation of reciprocity, the elements of recruitment, training, and rewards are separated by very little distance. Even the advent of full-time occupational specialization does little to upset this relationship in the nonliterate societies.

To explore the ramifications of economic organization in nonliterate societies the reader may consult other sources (Dalton, 1967; Herskovits, 1952; Nash, 1966). Suffice it to say here that the craftsman's reward is rarely in a form, such as money, which is directly convertible into all of the society's products. Instead his output is exchanged, sometimes indirectly, for other goods or services.

Motivations to technological activities are mainly imponderable. Moderns tend to emphasize the stimulus of economic gain and to downgrade other kinds of satisfactions. Nonliterates, on the other hand, do not rely on economic gain as a motivating force except in the case of some full-time specialized tasks.

In the simpler cultures biological necessity may be a prime motivating force because ever-present demands for food, shelter, and reproduction are strong. Ultimately these are the mainsprings of all human behavior, but factors other than such stark necessities usually account for production. Without the support of empirical research one might speculate that desires for diversity, novelty, and convenience may be at work.

This technological Gestalt is a major configuration which influences subsidiary elements as well. The product of one culture can be differentiated from the functionally similar product of another culture because the shape, the manner of execution, the materials, and the character of finish vary according to the culture which produced it.

Even without any graphic representation (for example, a blueprint), the technician works to execute specific designs which are of his culture, those with which he has a familiarity. The mental images or designs conjured up by the mention of an item are the goals toward which the craftsman strives. Such images condition his thinking about the entire work situation — his planning for tools and materials. Only when the technician becomes innovative does he depart from traditional designs. However, even under these circumstances a departure to a design completely removed from tradition is extremely unlikely. Studies of innovation (Barnett, 1953) stress the degree to which the innovator is forced to work with familiar elements. Design changes proceed by small increments, a fact attested to by many studies of design evolution. Perhaps they must do so to retain cultural acceptance.

The standards governing the primitive technologists' work may be more flexible than the designs. Because many nonspecialized persons are involved in production considerable variation occurs in their skill and products. Further, the frequent absence of full-time specialists inhibits the establishment of "professional" standards to which others might aspire. It is doubtful that comparison with the work of more skilled individuals would have this standard-setting effect.

To modern Westerners, who are constantly exposed to professional performance levels and often measure their own efforts by these, another attitudinal view may be difficult to comprehend. Yet some nonliterates measure performance on a sliding scale as when they judge the technical and other performances of children solely as those of children without reference to any adult standards. To use an old expression, in their eyes it is not remarkable that the bear dances so well but that it dances at all. The injection of professional standards into virtually all endeavors, from the playing of games to furniture-making, has inhibited the involvement of amateurs even though increasing leisure among Westerners has encouraged avocational pursuits. Exceptions lie in activities like basket-weaving which have hardly been professionalized in our societies and therefore present no such standards as models.

To a discussion of abstract performance standards must be added the evaluation of performance in each given work instance. Considerations of speed, cost, and permanence condition performance level, aside from any limitations imposed by the skill of the worker. The product, particularly if it is self-destructive, may not warrant substantial expenditure of time, skill, and care. When rocketry began in earnest, aerospace equipment manufacturers thought that their needs could be fulfilled by "cheap, quick, and dirty" work, since each rocket was to be used only once, unlike aircraft which were used time and again. They were quickly forced to an opposite position by the demand for one hundred percent reliability, a level not yet reached. However, this is an unusual situation and the more common requirement for "one-shot" items is the meeting of a minimal acceptable level. Köhler's famous chimpanzee found an unstable stack of boxes adequate to reach the overhead banana; that it collapsed immediately after he had reached the bait was unimportant.

A craftsman with great pride in his work may refuse to do less than his finest despite the demands of circumstances. Such a man cannot be hurried at his task, often to the dismay of those waiting for his product. To what extent such pride and a reluctance to lower standards is related to full-time involvement we cannot say. There probably is a positive correlation, however low.

Tools

Tools have had a central role in human history. Prehistorians have depended heavily on the development of tools — their shapes, functions, and materials — for use in the reconstruction of human history. For some the nature of the tool and its function have had as much significance and reality as have the products of tools.

The tool serves as an extender of the human body, more specifically of the hand and arm. It strengthens the grasp, protects the hand, magnifies the blow, lengthens the reach, increases precision of movement, and does many other things relevant to manipulation. More broadly defined, the tool aids any of the senses, largely through increasing their acuity and discrimination (e.g., a micrometer caliper). Generally, the earlier tools were not sense-extending, a refinement which has come in the past five centuries.

The making and use of tools is not an exclusively human characteristic: zoologists have reported instances of tool-making and tool-using by animals. However, though the use of tools may be frequent and often ingenious in the animal world, it never approaches the level or importance which it has assumed even among the most primitive peoples known to us. No animal seems to be as dependent upon tools as man is. Further, the difference in quantity, in itself sufficient to separate the animals from man, is accompanied by a difference in quality. Virtually from the start, human tool-making has been more complex in conception and execution than any made by animals.

As any hardware catalog will attest, our culture has a wide diversity of tools. The term tool, however, may be applied legitimately to a range of items far beyond those represented in such an inventory. Add to the present roster all those tools of times past but no longer found, and one is faced with a vast welter of materials to be analyzed and ordered.

Tool Typologies

The development of typological systems for tools has been of great importance to archeologists and prehistorians, who have had to rely on tools (among other recovered artifacts) for their conclusions. Discriminating criteria have included form, presumed use, and materials, singly or in combination.

Tool typologies based on form range from simple to highly complex. Outline forms, whether round, triangular, linear, and any projections from or indentations in these outlines are considered. Projectile point (arrow-, spear-point) typologies are frequently of this kind. For such tools the number and nature of points or edges must also be considered. It is, for example, the number of points which distinguishes the leister (or trident) from simple fishing spears. The nature of a cutting edge, smooth or serrated, straight or sinuous, may also be a differentiating criterion. The early hand axes of the Old World Lower Paleolithic Age were noted for their sinuous cutting edges, while later forms were substantially straight-edged.

In any group of tools, however homogenous, some differences in form may be found and used to distinguish subgroups or individual tools. Whether these differences are significant to anyone other than the typologist cannot always be known for despite the best efforts of the craftsman any two items he makes to the same specifications can be only nominally identical. Indeed, it is much more difficult to make by hand a series of supposedly identical items than a similar number of one-of-a-kind items. In dealing with typologies of form some allowance must be made for these random variations. If the sample is large enough the question of randomness, as contrasted with deliberation, may be answerable statistically. If the sample is small, then a substantially subjective judgment must be made, with attendant doubts.

The use of morphological typologies, whatever its shortcomings in other directions, does have the considerable merit of demonstrability. The forms and their differences are observable, whether other analysts agree with a given categorization or not. For this reason, if no other, this kind of typology has often been used and will doubtless be with us well into the future.

The use and function of prehistoric tools are more presumed than demonstrated. Only rarely is the tool found in such surroundings, in such juxtaposition to the work, as to make its use unequivocal. The use of an artifact is direct and immediate and may be profitably distinguished from function. The use of a pencil is to make marks on suitable surfaces; its function is to communicate ideas and sentiments. The use of a digging stick is to turn over the soil; its function is to cultivate gardens (Linton, 1936:404). The obvious relationship between use and function is easy to follow at this level but may not be so clear at complex levels and in archeological contexts. Additionally, the expected use-function relationship may come adrift under conditions in which an object becomes more symbolic than utilitarian. This occurs, for example, when the carrying (wearing) of a ballpoint pen or of eyeglasses becomes the status symbol of literacy instead of an aid to communication or vision. Efforts to strengthen the evidence for use and function and to reduce the element of presumption have followed some very interesting lines.

Inquiry into the making and use of tools in prehistoric times has been conducted in three different ways. First, attempts have been made to reconstruct experimentally the mode of manufacture of stone tools. Some prehistorians have been able to duplicate known types of chipped stone tools using methods which were presumably used in the past. Sufficient discrimination has been developed in the analysis of stone fractures to be reasonably sure that these reconstructions of technique are correct.

Support for these reconstructions is gained from observations of stoneworking by recent primitive people (Nelson, 1931). It would be erroneous to draw a simple equation between the work of these recent people and that of ancient man, even though their products are similar. To do so would assume that no technical advances had been made in several millenia, whereas the archeological record provides, in the artifacts recovered, substantial evidence for such advances. Despite this caution there is value in the study of recent primitive stonework. Reconstructions by modern Westerners, who are often naive about stoneworking, may well be influenced by the sophistication which they have in other technological areas and may therefore be suspect. By contrast the stonework of recent primitives, though it reflects a legacy of long experience in this medium, is less likely to be modified by other, more modern, traditions of tool production.

Second, through the use of original or duplicated tools on various materials and in various ways knowledge has been acquired of the manner in which the working edges wear. It is now possible to distinguish archeologically-recovered tools which, for example, were used to cut or scrape wood from those which were used on hides or for butchering. The character of micro-fracture on the working edge, scratches in the tool material, and the angle at which the worn edge stabilizes (ceases to wear further) are all products of the particular work situation. It is probably not possible to sketch these conditions in any but the broadest detail, but once the outlines have been set the individual researcher can determine the particulars of his context. One would have to conduct some experiments with the materials actually used, as each kind of stone may differ by locality from that used in the prototype experiments. Similarly, woods would differ; though hide, flesh, and bone are fairly homogenous in their effects on the tools.

Such knowledge about tool wear can provide the archeologist with a better estimate of the amount and type of work done at each site. If it is known that tools are quickly dulled by a particular use, say the scraping of hides, then the presence of many such worn tools no longer implies that large numbers of hides were scraped (Keller, 1966; Semenov, 1957).

Third, the relative efficiency of different types of stone and metal tools has been explored through experimental use. Careful control of the experimental situation reduced individual and situational variations to the point where objective comparisons could be made. These experimental results are especially important to evaluations of cultural advances presumed to have accompanied changes in tools (Steensberg, 1943; Iversen, 1956). While the outcomes of these and other related studies have been valuable and interesting, much remains to be done along these lines.

Typologies based on use may relate to the particular application or action of the tool or to the assignment of a tool to a given technological area. In the former categorization one would find reference to striking tools (e.g., hammers), cutting tools (knives, saws), piercing tools (awls, drills), and, perhaps, scraping tools. Each group can be further divided, and some can merge with other categories, as with the ax which strikes to cut. Except for some evident problems, this categorization is simple and may be unenlightening. In the latter categorization — by association with a technological area — problems result from multiple uses. The same tool may find its way into several technologies — especially in the simpler tool inventories and in the absence of occupational specialization. The same knife which is used in the harvest may also cut thatching for the house, pare vegetables for cooking, be used in making a bow, and serve as a weapon of war. Scholars are convinced that many tools of the Lower and Middle Paleolithic cultural period had multiple uses.

Nonetheless, use typologies can be of value in assessing overall tool-using habits. The proportions of tools of each type within the total inventory may reveal cultural preferences for kinds of materials worked.

If such preferences are known to exist from other evidence, compensation in analysis can be made for this variable. One may find, on balance, that the workers in question showed a predisposition or partiality toward some tools and virtually ignored others which were present. An entire culture may demonstrate a preference, as illustrated in the use of a D-handled adz in some tribes of the Canadian Northwest Coast (see Figure 1). The preference may extend to groups of tools similarly used.

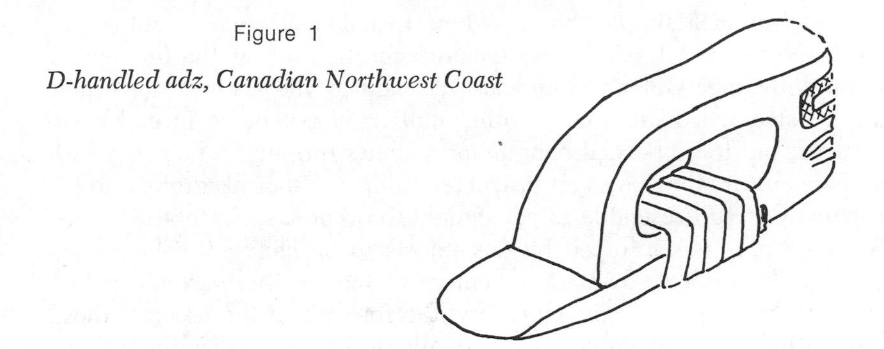

Figure 1

D-handled adz, Canadian Northwest Coast

Typologies based on materials are among the oldest known to scholars who from the early nineteenth century have recognized a progression of prehistoric cultural ages based on the replacement of one tool material by another. The Stone Ages (Paleolithic, Mesolithic, and Neolithic) were succeeded by the Metal Ages (Copper, Bronze, and Iron). This mode of designation of a tool's material carried some immediate implications regarding its placement in the chronological order, though no material was promptly and completely displaced by its successor. Stone tools continued to be made during the prehistoric metal ages and some few, such as the agate mortar and pestle, persist today. Metals also have differential characteristics such that an earlier metal might be better suited for a given purpose than a later one. Copper hammers, for example, are useful in that they produce less marring of the workpiece than do steel hammers; bronze punches are regularly used for the same reason. The nonmagnetic nature of these two ancient metals also keeps them on the modern scene.

Materials typologies, also based on readily observable facts, have been convenient for archeologists who can usually make judgments about the materials without recourse to specialists. Through the materials employed one may learn something of the traveling and trading habits of prehistoric peoples. Evidence of substantial processing before use indicates a degree of technological sophistication. Applied in a simple fashion, typologies of materials serve only as a basis for sorting artifacts, adding nothing to the situation but order, which can be unrewarding.

Motor Habit Patterns

Motor habits are the dynamic side of tool use. Without being manipulated, even indirectly, the tools remain static and of no consequence.

The members of all cultures have learned from their fellows certain ways of moving and holding the body. By imitation and instruction the child internalizes postures and movements in the same manner as other aspects of culture. Children learn how to eat — not only the etiquette of the table, but such simple things as how to hold and manipulate eating utensils. Writing instruction also includes the holding of the implement and the movements of hand and arm as well as the symbols and their usage. Instruction in the use of other tools may not be so formal or so prolonged, but it is a part, also, of an individual's training. The new member of the culture thus becomes instructed in the ways of his group and his manipulations will resemble rather closely those of his mentors.

Such learning is reinforced by the objects to be handled. The novice is presented with a ready-made inventory of tools to be mastered in the style of his compatriots. The inventory, the forms, and the uses are those of his culture. He may, perhaps, eventually add to or modify these tools, but initially he can do little more than accept or reject them. The tools themselves provide some guidance for his actions because they lend themselves, in one way or another, to manipulation in a given fashion and inhibit other responses.

Ultimately, the behavior of the individual in these manipulations becomes effortless, habitual, and "automatic." Only when one tries to break out of the routine, for example, when attempting "mirror writing," does the grip of habit become apparent.

Different tools tend to fall into classes which can be similarly manipulated. For example, hammers of all kinds are handled in much the same way as are saws, files, and other groups; each individual tool does not have its own unique style of manipulations. Since the motor habits (habits of muscular action) men use with their tools are parts of culture, they are subject to the "patterning" phenomenon. This means that the culturally-conditioned responses are not randomly assorted, but fall into coherent groups.

The formation of pervasive motor habit patterns is the end result of these influences in which learning, habituation, the tool inventory, and economy of operation all play a part. The Western habit of writing from left to right is paralleled by the manner in which we write a series of numbers. The captions of news photographs name the people pictured from left to right, and so on. The writing patterns are, of course, reflected in the reading patterns which include the controlled movements of the eye as well as a particular mode of thought.

Motor habit patterns are so much a part of us that we take them for granted. Only when we see a sharp contrast between our habits and those of others is the artificiality, i.e., the cultural dictation, of the situation apparent. A fine comparison can be drawn between a Western European pattern and one from the Far East. The teeth of European hand saws are raked or inclined away from the handle to cut on the push stroke, that is, as they are moved away from the body of the user. There are, admittedly, some exceptions to this rule such as the two-man crosscut saw and the coping saw. By contrast, Far Easterners use pull saws with teeth raked toward the handle to cut as the tool is pulled toward the operator (see Figure 2). There are no known exceptions to the rule except tools which have been introduced from the West. Emphasis to the rule is provided by a form of two-man saw reported from China. The teeth of this saw are raked toward each end from the center; each half of the saw then displays directionality. Presumably each sawyer does most of his work during the first half of the saw's movement toward him (Hommel, 1937:228).

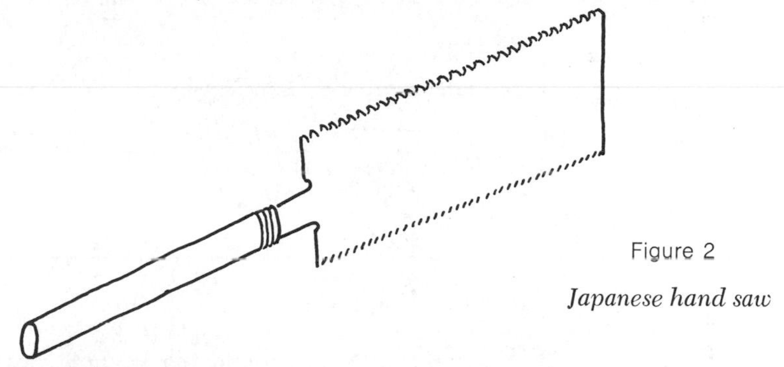

Figure 2

Japanese hand saw

Patterning of motor habits would not be so evident if we were to compare only saws and their manner of use. The push pattern of the West and the Far Eastern pull pattern carry over into other tools as well. Western planes, with the exception of a few specialized forms, are generally pushed to cut. Far Eastern planes follow the pattern of the saws and are used to cut on the pull stroke, drawn toward the operator.

These differences are not found solely between the Atlantic and Pacific shores of Eurasia. Scattered, but probably reliable, reports indicate that the Turks, who migrated to their present location from Central Asia, follow some of the Far Eastern pattern. One might expect to find this pull pattern also in parts of the Balkans, which were formerly under Turkish domination (Chapelle, 1957:16).

Other large geographic areas, each containing several cultures, display this same kind of patterning to tool use. Africans, south of the Sahara, have many tools which operate on the pull stroke or as they are moved downward. The hoe and the adz, both pull tools, are characteristic. Even knives, whose direction of use may be somewhat optional, are drawn toward the user. The American Indians, if any characterization is possible, show some tendency toward a predominance of pull tools, primarily knives and adzes.

The common pattern for push tools among western Europeans, which we take for granted as "normal," is the minority practice among peoples of the world. There is some indication that Europe of a century or more ago made greater use of pull tools (drawknives, spoke-shaves, scorps, and adzes) than at the present time; in the United States only the spoke-shave survives as a pull tool offered by some of the major manufacturers.

The habits of use and the design of tools interact with each other; the rake of saw teeth, the curvature of a knife blade (see Figure 3), and the location and nature of handles are all related to the manner of use. These features, the products of habits, also create or reinforce habits, especially for the novice. Habits of use are reflected less obviously in the capabilities

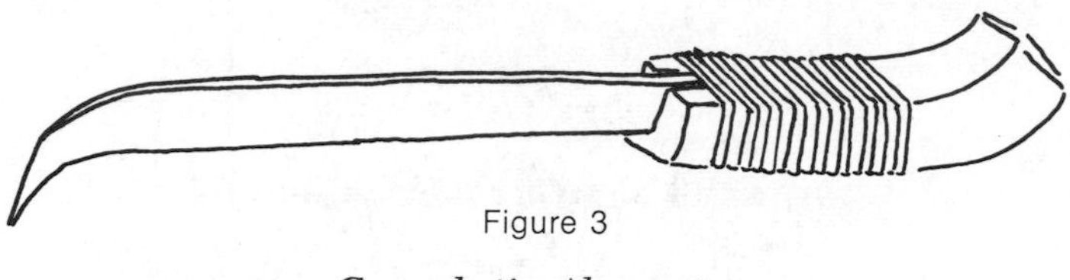

Figure 3

Canoe knife, Algonquian

of the tools themselves. The author was first introduced to Japanese saws by an acquaintance (a Westerner) who had found the keyhole saws to be superior in operation to those of European style. Cutting on the pull stroke, the thin blade of the Japanese keyhole saw was less likely to buckle than a saw which was pushed to cut. For equal strength, in the direction of proper operation, the Japanese keyhole saw could be thinner and narrower than its European counterpart, and so cut holes with smaller radii. The same relative strength of cutting is also true of other thin-blade Japanese saws. They can make finer cuts and waste less wood in the process. Though modern Japanese saws are of good quality steel, the pull saw generally can be effective even when made of inferior materials that survive stress under tension but do not adequately resist compressive stresses.

Motor habits can be reconstructed from the tools of the past which survive archeologically. The form of the tool and the wear to which it is subjected are closely related to the manner of its use. Though presently we are limited in the conclusions which may be drawn from these data, further study and experimentation may make possible eventual command of this kind of evidence.

Technological Continuity

Technological history displays, perhaps more than most cultural aspects, a continuity from the remote past to the present day. Each advance depended so much, physically, on certain antecedents that sharp breaks with the past are rare. Nevertheless, from time to time there occurred major advances or departures into new directions which H. S. Harrison would call discoveries, "revelations of the unpredictable, or at least the unpredicted" (Harrison, 1930:107). These include stone chipping, ceramics, metals produced from ores, the wheel and axle, and power production from internal combustion — great advances which may not represent any higher order of thought than some other changes, but which became sources of further developments.

The history of tools parallels that of technology generally, but with fewer discontinuities. Many modern hand tools are remarkably like their predecessors of a century or more ago, except for the substitution of modern materials and the addition of electric or pneumatic power. Few new approaches are attempted since the power tools reproduce the principles and movements of the hand tools.

Some Tool Histories

Three historic groups of tools, primarily those used in woodworking, are discernible. The first group contains the ax, the adz, the knife, the chisel, and various scrapers; the second consists of drills, and the last includes saws and planes.

Early Edge Tools. Most tools of the first group are identifiable, as differentiated forms, from the Middle Paleolithic period to the present day. The stone versions, first chipped and later ground into shape, persist through the Neolithic cultural period. In the Mesolithic period in northern Europe some were also made of antler and bone. The Metal Ages saw the gradual introduction of copper, then bronze, and finally iron (mild steel) as tool materials, but because the metal tools were initially rare, expensive, and qualitatively rather poor, the displacement of stone by metal was a slow process. Tools made from stone and other nonmetallic materials, because they were the traditional forms, persisted for certain ceremonial purposes as well.

During this transitional period the metal tools, and especially metal weapons, must have had prestige value, as they have been found in surroundings which suggest ownership by the upper classes. Hoards of metal weapons occur in the remains of Near Eastern palaces and some were buried with individuals who, on the basis of richness of other grave goods, are identified as having been socially outstanding. While the upper class had metal goods, the lesser people continued to use stone tools and tried to approximate the metal tools they lacked. In the Baltic region ground stone axes have been found that are shaped like Bronze Age cast bronze axes. These stone replicas are such slavish copies that they even show the lines which were formed on the bronze originals where the halves of the mold met. On the stone replicas, of course, these lines had absolutely no utilitarian purpose.

Because handles are much more perishable than stone blades and correspondingly less likely to be recovered, direct evidence for hafting tools (that is, equipping them with handles) is later in prehistory than the appearance of the stone tools themselves. The adaptation of the stone blades for hafting often calls for certain modifications in shape: flat faces of a blade may be fluted to fit into a forked shaft, a tang may be provided which can be lashed into the split end of a handle, or a groove, to accommodate a haft or its lashing, may be worked into the stone. These provide indirect evidence that handles, though missing, were used. Even in the absence of tangs, flutes, grooves, and similar points for attachment of handles, there sometimes is evidence of their presence. The lashing of sinew, rawhide, or fiber, the coating of any adhesive used, and the handle itself all serve to protect the part of the stone which they cover from random scarring, sometimes leaving areas in comparatively mint condition, as they were originally worked into shape.

Hafting was commonly employed during the Mesolithic period for a wide variety of tools, and it continued as the general practice thereafter. How much earlier one may trace this practice is debatable. Projectile shafts — darts, lances, and harpoons — had points (not necessarily of stone) fastened to them during the Upper Paleolithic period. The form of Levallois points, which had flutes on their broad faces, suggests that they were fastened into split shafts in Middle Paleolithic times. One cannot say with certainty that many tools or weapons of the Middle Paleolithic were hafted.

Drills. Drills, forming the second historic group, make a definite appearance in the Upper Paleolithic cultural period. These chipped stone tools had short points with somewhat tapered edges. The resulting holes were often subconical and did not pass through much of the material drilled. Making holes in thick materials was sometimes accomplished by drilling from one side to the full reach of the drill and then back-drilling from the reverse side to meet the first hole. Holes formed in this fashion have a characteristic biconical profile.

The stone drill points and many of the later metal types had rhomboidal or lozenge-shaped cross sections. They were chip cutters, but none cut the continuous curls which may be produced with modern drill bits. Flutes and variant tip forms appeared in the late Middle Ages. The helical fluting, especially around a solid center, seen in modern augers and twist drills, is only a few centuries old.

One cannot expect that helically fluted drills would have appeared at an early date. All of the early drills cut equally well when rotated in either direction. The helical style is, of course, monodirectional. It is important to note that virtually all hand drilling up to the nineteenth century, except that with the bit brace, was bidirectional. The drill bits or points reflect this circumstance.

The devices used to revolve drill bits originate with the unaided hand, the wrist, and the forearm. This suggests that the motion was rotatory but with the direction reversed after one-third to one-half a revolution. The simple drill shaft twirled between the palms had the same reversal of rotation, perhaps each three to six revolutions. In fact, this is true of virtually all drills until the most recent. In keeping with its presumed antiquity, the palm drill was almost world-wide; where it was not found historically there is reason to believe that it was superseded by advanced types.

An improvement over the palm drill is the bow drill which substitutes a light bow's reciprocating motion for that of the palm (see Figure 4).

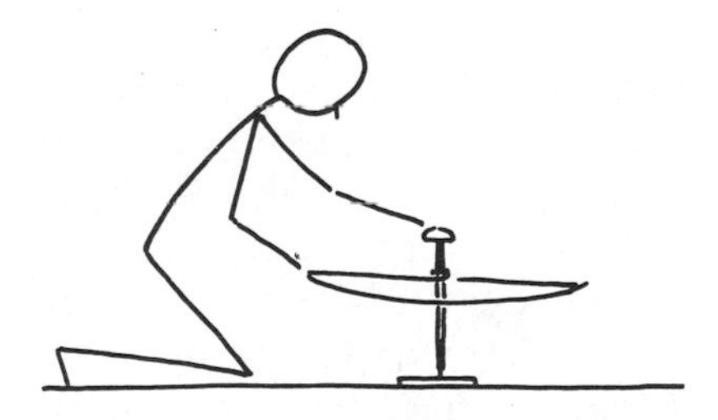

Figure 4 *Bow drill*

The bow string is carried a turn or two around the drill shaft; movement of the bow causes the shaft to turn. With the palm drill no other means is needed to hold the drill shaft upright, however the bow drill's use requires a cap or holder in which the upper end of the drill shaft revolves. The drill operator holds the bow in one hand and the cap in the other.

The Eskimos produced a variant cap which could be gripped in the teeth, freeing a hand to steady the work. The strap drill (Figure 5), or thong drill, is like the bow drill but lacks the bow. With the mouth-held cap each end of the thong may be held in a hand and the whole controlled by a single operator. If two people are available, one operates the thong

Figure 5
Strap drill with two operators

while the other holds the cap and the work. The bow drill was known over northern Asia and northern North America. Refined forms, factory-made, were used in eighteenth- and nineteenth-century Europe. The strap drill seems to have been confined to China and the Eskimos.

The pump drill (Figure 6) approximates the rotational capabilities of the bow drill, but can apply less pressure. A crosspiece, often with a central hole, is brought to the drill shaft. Cords or thongs of equal length connect the ends of the crosspiece to the top of the shaft. To start the drill

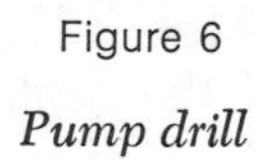

Figure 6
Pump drill

its shaft is turned several revolutions in one direction to wind the cords around the shaft and cause the crosspiece to rise. The crosspiece is then pressed down, causing the shaft to revolve. As the crosspiece reaches the bottom of its travel downward pressure is slackened while the shaft continues to rotate and winds the cords in the opposite direction. Pressure is then applied and the cycle repeated. A rhythm developed by the operator keeps the drill running smoothly. To provide adequate rotational momentum to rewind the cords most pump drills need a flywheel which is usually placed toward the bottom of the shaft. A simple crosspiece may be fastened to the shaft in lieu of a round flywheel. The pump drill was used in the Far East, among the Eskimo, and historically in Europe.

Though not a part of any primitive people's tool inventory, the Archimedean drill (Figure 7) is an old form which persists in Europe today. The metal drill shaft, which may turn freely in a top handle, has a helical flute cut in it or is itself helically twisted. A runner with a corresponding

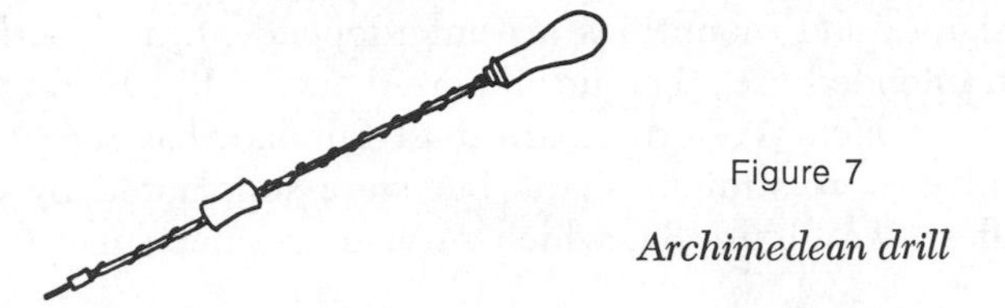

Figure 7
Archimedean drill

internal flute surrounds the shaft. The handle is steadied, and the runner is moved along the shaft causing the shaft to turn a dozen revolutions or so in one direction and then to reverse rotation as the runner is brought back. The reciprocating movement of the runner is continued to maintain drilling. The bits used with this drill have a single flute on one side so as to be nondirectional in cutting characteristics.

These early drills and drill points reflect an important fact about the mechanics of their era: continuous rotary motion was rare. Until comparatively recently, only those devices which were cranked by hand, such as the quern and the grindstone, could rotate indefinitely in one direction. The remainder turned, for comparatively few revolutions, first in one direction and then the other.

Later Edge Tools. Saws and planes, the third historic group, have been developed in the more elaborate technologies and are not, in the main, important among primitives.

Tool inventories in chipped stone, but usually of Neolithic age, sometimes include blades with toothed or serrated edges with a saw-like character which differed in use from present day saws. For one thing, the blades were not so parallel-sided as to make indefinite sawing into a piece of wood possible; the blade cut a kerf narrower than its maximum thickness and so would soon bind in the cut. Other ancient saw types included a blade made from a laminar stone such as slate. Used with an abrasive mud or paste it would cut (actually grind) its way through stone. Back-cutting, like back-drilling, was commonly employed on thick material. Like modern stone-cutting saws, the early forms had no teeth.

The metal saws can be traced as early as Dynastic Egypt. The blades were of bronze, the teeth were not set, and the blade had no taper from edge to back. Wedging and lubricating kept the saw from binding in the cut. The setting of a saw involved turning some or all of the teeth alternately outward from the plane of the blade. This modification made the saw cut a kerf which is wider than the blade thickness and reduced binding. For this reason the classic Romans set their saws. A taper in blade thickness, from edge to back, is another solution to the binding problem. Some eighteenth-century European hand saws display this taper as a substitute for the setting of teeth. Modern hand saws, which have more or less set, have an almost imperceptible blade taper.

Blade shapes and mountings are interdependent, and both are correlated with intended use. The unsupported, sword-like blade with an end handle, with which Westerners are most familiar, has temporal priority. Early handles were straight shafts but were supplanted by open pistol-grip handles (see Figure 8), which survive on some small saws. By the

Figure 8

Pistol-grip hand saw

eighteenth century in Europe the open handle was giving way to a closed handle of modern type. Saws of this sort were generally used for crosscutting wood. Supported blades were held in a frame under tension which made them less likely to buckle; they could also be thinner and narrower. The frames held the blade at one side, like the recent bucksaw, or between two stringers. The side-mounted blade could be fixed in the plane of the frame for crosscutting or at right angles to this plane for ripping. Some frames were designed so that the blade could be turned while under tension to cut curves in the style of a large coping saw. The framed saws with central blades were for ripping and had the blade at right angles to the frame plane. All of the framed saws could be readily dismantled so that the blade could be started through a hole in the work. Large unframed saws, the big crosscut- and pit-saws had one handle easily removable for the same reason.

The carpenter's plane may trace its ancestry to the earliest scrapers, yet many tools which ornament its family tree have survived to the present. Stone tools, functionally classified as scrapers, were present by the Middle Paleolithic cultural period. We can speculate that some earlier flakes were also used for scraping. Stone scrapers were so successful that metal ones, of deliberate manufacture as opposed to adventitiously-used scraps, were not important until the Iron Age. Even after the advent of steel scrapers, glass scrapers were used because a fresh, sharp edge could easily be made.

Closely allied to the plane are the drawknife and the scorp (scorper, scauper, round shave) which have the single bevel of the plane iron. The drawknife blade is usually straight, flanked by two handles with which it may be pulled (drawn) toward the operator (see Figure 9). Depth of cut is controlled by varying the angle of pull and by using the tool either bevel up or down. In the hands of the unskilled a drawknife may cut too deeply. The scorp (Figure 10) is a specialized, curved drawknife which in one form has two handles and a cutting edge around

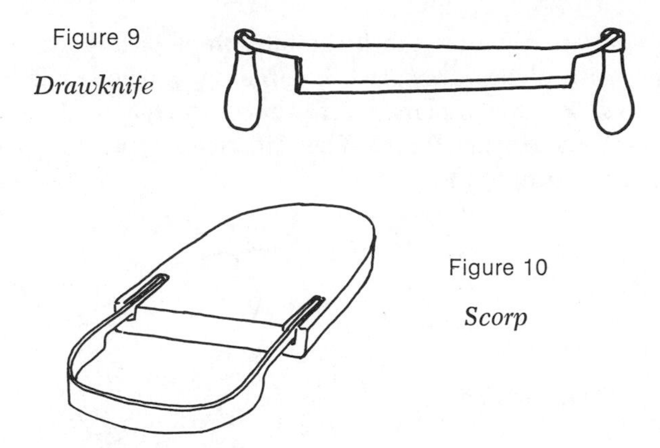

Figure 9

Drawknife

Figure 10

Scorp

180 to 270 degrees of a circle. Alternatively, the blade may be circular, though not sharpened its entire length, and attached to a single handle. The scorp was used in the making of hollowed woodenware, troughs, gutters, and some cooperage.

In neither the drawknife nor the scorp is the depth of cut controlled by anything other than the operator's skill. By contrast the spokeshave (Figure 11), like the plane, has a controllable depth of cut. This is accomplished in the simpler models by varying the distance between the blade and the base, or sole, of the tool. Additionally, the leading edge of the sole is ahead of the blade so that the tool may be rotated about its lateral axis to increase or diminish the cut. The recent version of the spokeshave is really a miniature plane. The blade projects through a throat below the level of the sole. The degree of projection controls the cut, with the chips passing upward through the throat. The handles of the spokeshave project laterally, in substantial alignment with the cutting edge, rather than toward the operator. Like the drawknife, the spokeshave is a pull tool.

Figure 11 *Spokeshave*

The plane in forms approaching the modern is, paradoxically, both early and late. Archeological evidence shows that the Romans of the early Christian era had all-metal and composite planes which were the equal of late nineteenth-century European and American models. After this early efflorescence, the tool went into an eclipse lasting over a millenium. It reappeared with crude forms of wood except for the blade or iron. So matters remained until the late nineteenth century when American composite planes appeared, combining a wooden body with metal upper works. European planes were slower to change, and wooden planes are still made and used there. The American types have been solely of metal since the turn of the century.

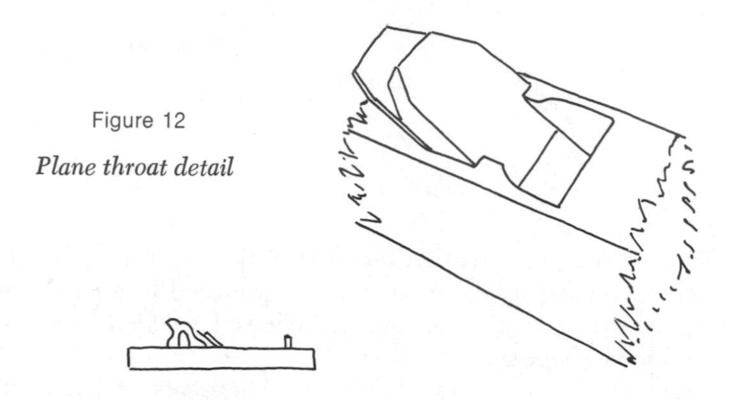

Figure 12

Plane throat detail

The plane iron is held in place by a wedge in most European planes; the wedge fits down into the throat on top of the iron and is held in place by shoulders on either side (see Figure 12). Adjustment of the iron is accomplished by loosening the wedge, setting the iron, and tightening the wedge. This was a sufficiently arduous task so a carpenter often kept at hand two or more similar planes set for differing degrees of cut. A difference in mounting of the iron is observable between European and Far Eastern planes. In the latter the iron may be very thick and tapered toward the cutting edge; it serves as its own wedge, being held under shoulders on either side of the throat (see Figure 13). Alternatively, the iron may be of conventional thickness but held in place by a wedge under a dowel across the opening of the throat as in Figure 14.

Traditionally, Westerners have used the plane as a push tool. Though handles may be added, as they have been recently, they are not necessary. The simpler wooden planes have no handles at all. The Far Eastern planes, and possibly those in the Turkish world, are prevailingly pulled to cut. In many examples this habit of use is reflected in the presence of cross handles (compare with our vertical handles). However, cross handles are not infallible indicators of the pulling habit for they did occur on some Scandinavian planes which were pushed to cut.

The plane was a great advance over the scraper in that it gave a precisely-controlled cut. The long sole of the plane made it possible to

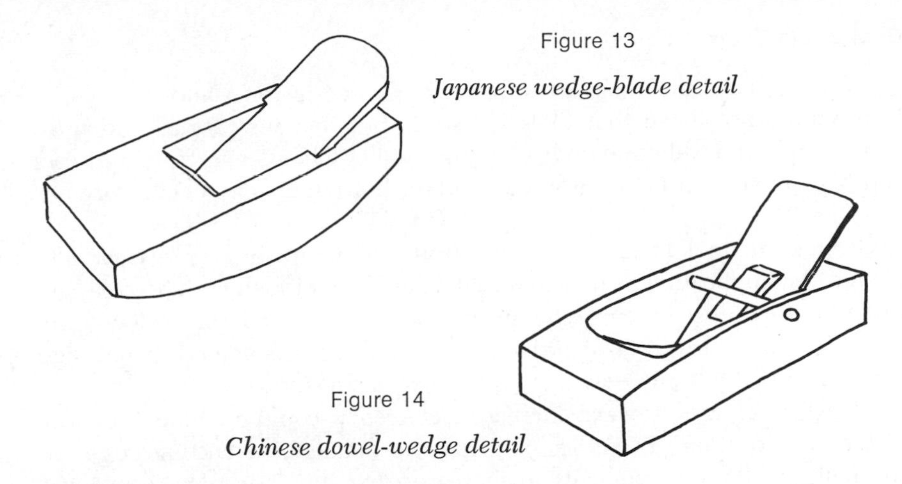

Figure 13

Japanese wedge-blade detail

Figure 14

Chinese dowel-wedge detail

smooth surfaces to substantial flatness. In addition this comparatively sophisticated tool was characteristic only of more technologically-advanced peoples. Many skilled craftsmen worked without it for a long period of time.

Primary Versus Secondary Tools

Primary tools as distinguished from secondary and tertiary tools are those which are directly applied to work, whose product is "consumable" without further substantial steps. The ax, the hoe, and the scraper are examples of primary tools. The secondary tool is one which makes other tools, usually primary tools. The blacksmith's hammer and the Upper Paleolithic burin (graver) exemplify secondary tools. Tertiary tools, which make secondary tools are exemplified by a device for making tool bits for machine lathes.

The classification of tools as primary, secondary, and tertiary is not based on the nature of the tool alone but on the use to which the tool is put. A knife is a primary tool when it is butchering an animal carcass for cooking but a secondary tool when it is trimming a projectile weapon shaft. The classification as originally intended provides a measure of the technological sophistication of a culture. The more highly developed the technology, presumably the more specialized and refined the tools. One would expect few, if any, tertiary tools among savages. However, any such classification must be based on the tool and its usage rather than the tool by itself. One must be certain that the attribution of use is that of the culture examined and not the use to which the same tool is put in another culture.

Changes in Tools

As parts of culture tools are subject to change in form and use. Continuity does not mean that tools are static but that new forms and uses can be seen as developments from earlier tools. Changes in form and use can have reciprocal bearing on each other, but either may occur without the other.

Changes in tool form may result from efforts toward increased efficiency, the application of new materials, the effect of fashion in design, integration of diffused items, change in pertinent motor habits, change in use, and from "drift." The order in which these are named is not significant, and the list is only suggestive not exhaustive.

Changes directed toward increased efficiency could include the provision or relocation of handles or grips, the details of a cutting edge, or the multiplication of elements to increase capacity. These are more apt to occur before the item has been adapted to current applications. The application of new materials will bring about changes as their potentialities and limitations are explored and exploited. Increase in material strength can be reflected in greater strength of a tool and some differences in its handling, as well as thinner, possibly lighter, construction. The production of the tool may be changed, as from casting to forging, with attendant changes in form — outlines, indents and undercuts, radii of curvatures, smoothness of surface, persistence of flaws and other work marks. Certainly the change from ground stone axes in the Neolithic to cast copper and bronze axes of later ages was accompanied by changes in form which made new modes of hafting possible. The same might be said of an earlier change which saw the introduction of antler axes in some phases of the European Mesolithic Age.

Changes in form resulting from design fashions are easy to observe in the twentieth century, but prehistoric illustrations are more difficult to find. Perhaps fashion, which we commonly associate with personal adornment, was not so widely felt in other aspects of culture in earlier times. Thus the widespread adoption of streamlining, itself nominally a functional response to reduction of wind resistance and obviously unnecessary for aerodynamic efficiency in most of its applications, did lead to clearer, less cluttered designs. Nothing comparable is evident in prehistoric tools and weapons, but pottery clearly responded to fashion in designs while retaining its utilitarian aspects. Would it be legitimate to consider that this makes the case for fashion response in prehistoric tools?

Integration following diffusion can bring about changes in tool form as the new tool is brought into consonance with existing tools in the inventory. The tools followed as models may be those of the same general technology and similar in certain salient points to those of the same presumed origin. Such a process will make an item, perhaps borrowed from institutional kitchens, come to look like a domestic kitchen utensil.

Change in pertinent motor habits would certainly be expected to have some reflection in tool forms. Tools, generally, indicate the way in which they are held and used. However, it is improbable that any fundamental change would occur in the motor habits related to use of a given tool. The more likely prospect is that the tool itself would fall out of use and be replaced by another employed in a style congruent to the new habits.

New or altered uses may have consequences in the form of tools. As machine tools come to be used more frequently, the hand-powered tools which they replace are reduced to a secondary-use status. The hand tools are used when the job is too small to warrant employment of a power tool or the care of a full-fledged operation or when the worker is an amateur in the area of the particular job or the job is undercapitalized and exchanges labor for equipment. The lowered status and employment of the tool is probably reflected in its lower quality — of materials, finish, sturdiness, and so forth. No longer the prime means of accomplishing the task, the hand-powered tool is now intended for use by second-raters, if it continues to be made at all. With the advent of power jointers, sanders, planers, and routers, many of the older uses of the carpenter's hand plane are disappearing, and planes for jointing are no longer made.

Cultural drift may make its effects felt in the realm of technology and tools, as in other aspects of culture. Conceptually related to genetic and linguistic drift, cultural drift refers to changes which occur in a random and directionless manner as the result of chance. One might cite here the possible result from the behavior of material which resists forming in the usual way, or an interruption which causes a craftsman to overlook one step in production. Because this is a random process, it is difficult to be explicit either about the causes or the results. However, it is certain that drift has occurred and has affected tool forms through history.

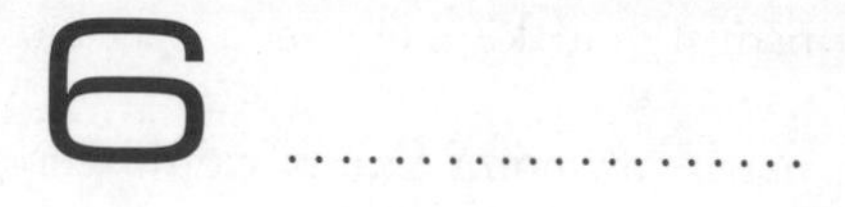

6

Materials

Simpler technologies are often distinguishable from more complex technologies by their heavy dependence on a limited number of natural materials which are not extensively processed. When synthetic materials do occur, they are usually few in number and the product of simple processes. Restriction of the material repertoire in this fashion leads to a certain sameness in the products and methods of production of a group of related cultures.

Our view of the materials of the prehistoric past, known only through archeological investigations, is doubtless distorted by the factor of perishability. Certainly the people of the European Lower Paleolithic cultural age used materials other than the stone which has survived. The chance recovery of two wooden spear shafts from this time confirms what common sense would dictate (Movius, 1950; Oakley, 1950). Bone and antler tools from this age are rare (or some say debatable) but are to be expected (Dart, 1957). For the Middle and Upper Paleolithic periods we have abundant evidence of stone, bone, and antler, though wooden remains are still occasional.

The increasing ability of man to modify what he found was as important as the gradual growth of the materials inventory. The earlier material uses were of stones, limbs, clays, and so forth in substantially the state in which they were found. A piece of wood which approximated the dimensions of the finished item could be used directly. Time spent seeking such a piece was not wasted when one considers the arduous labor that would have been required to work down a larger piece. The close relation between natural material and the finished product, or a part of it, led to advance selection of suitable materials and occasionally to their modification during the growing stage. The earmarking of certain trees as "canoe trees" in the Pacific islands exemplifies the former practice; the bending of growing shrubs to form the loop of a "mush stirrer" (actually a hot-stone-handling tool) in aboriginal California exemplifies the latter (Kroeber, 1925:446).

Man progressed from the selection of randomly occurring desirable specimens to modifying their occurrence as in planting fields with a given plant. Dense stands of a single plant rarely occur in nature. In addition to altering the occurrence of a desired plant, it has been possible, recently, to produce uniformity, essential when fitting plants to machines, such as harvesters. This, of course, was of substantially less importance to simpler peoples.

An allied specialization in plant cultivation is the growth of plants for some unusual purpose. A modern case would be the cultivation of a special type of corn (maize), not for the kernels, but for the cobs which are used in making tobacco pipes. At one time a plant probably produced more than one usable product — a fruit, fibers, oil, wood — but was grown for only one of its potentialities. The different logic for the utilization of animal resources has been examined elsewhere (Lowie, 1940:51).

The increasing ability of man to process his materials is reflected in the difference between wood as used by most simpler peoples and its many precut forms today. Through the application of machines and the development of standards, it is possible to produce wood in a series of shapes simultaneously generic and specific. Many pieces have probable specific uses in construction or cabinet work, such as flooring, shingles, or molding; others, such as plywood, are generally useful. It is doubtful that any man, prior to the introduction of the power saw, ever cut a log into pieces without knowing in advance just how each piece would be used.

There is a midway point between the specific piece-for-a-job and the generic lumber-for-anything positions. Recently, perhaps to the present day, the Japanese sawyers kept together the planks sawn from a single log. This group of boards was tied into a bundle and presumably separated only after deliberation. The use of related pieces of one origin made possible the showing of "butterfly" (mirror image) grain patterns on adjacent panels. The two halves of the whole pattern are the pieces separated by a single saw cut.

Production of synthetic materials is a gauge of technological advancement. Simpler peoples generally use things as they find them. People with advanced technologies are rarely satisfied with natural materials as they come to hand but instead reformulate, alter, and modify them in many ways. It is a part of modernism to be able to do this; perhaps it is also a part of modernism to be impelled to follow up the capability.

In speaking of synthetic material we mean one or more of the following: (1) a material of natural origin which, through extensive processing, assumes a new character, such as leather; (2) a material made from a natural raw material, which is radically different from its raw source, as ceramics made from clay; (3) a material which strongly resembles a given natural material but is not derived in the usual natural manner, such as a synthetic gem stone; (4) a material which is totally synthetic and has no counterpart in nature, such as nylon. The progression of degrees of synthesis in these several definitions provides an insight into the several steps through which technological history has passed. The first two definitions apply readily to the simpler technologies; the last two apply virtually exclusively to modern technologies. The difference between the two pairs is, indeed, the advancement.

Inferentially, leather, or at least processed hide, was known during the Upper Paleolithic period. We have found tools which are construed to have been hide scrapers, other tools thought to have been awls, and some which were undoubtedly needles. Together they imply the making of garments of hides or leather. Some occasional archeological sites of the Mesolithic period, such as the Danish bog sites, have even yielded up bits of leather.

Ceramics were the leading synthetic materials of prehistory. Pottery, the major product in this material, is a hallmark of the Neolithic period. There are, in fact, some who are disinclined to recognize a Neolithic culture without pottery or who consider that a plant-cultivating culture without pottery is of a special type.

The metals represent a second illustration of those natural materials whose processed form is radically altered. Only native ("float") copper and some precious metals are found in the metallic state and are usable without smelting. Such metals were early noted and used by primitive peoples. The ability to engage in widespread metallurgical activities employing heat treatment, annealing (of copper) rather than smelting, was virtually contemporaneous with the early stirrings of the Neolithic (Wertime, 1964). It was not until several millenia later that metals made a substantial technological impact.

Without discussing specific artifacts, it is possible to comment generally on shaping and fastening, both of which are closely related to use of materials. Often, the products of simpler technologies are of a single piece of material. A housepost, a simple arrow shaft, or a net ring may illustrate this point. The attempt to work within the confines of a single piece may influence the product, as in the African wood carving which is within the bounds of the original log. The habit of making a mast of a single spar will limit the practical height of masts until someone begins to add topmasts. The single-piece-syndrome will also lead to the conservation of potentially useful pieces, as the "canoe tree" mentioned earlier, and to much searching for just the right piece instead of making a composite substitute. Obviously, making a product of a single piece obviates the need for fastenings.

Fastenings in most primitive technologies are nonmetallic because most of these technologies lack metal or substantial quantities of it. In place of metal nails, screws, and bolts we find lashings, pegs, adhesives, one-piece construction, and self-holding forms.

Though much underrated today by Westerners, lashings are very effective fasteners. Moreover, the lashing may well be one of the oldest fastenings for it probably held, at least in part, the projectile points of the Upper Paleolithic. Through careful choice of materials and attention to detail it is possible to hold quite irregular pieces in place with lashing. Imagine, if you will, trying to fasten a stone to the end of a board with any common metallic fastening of today. Lashings, however, can be self-tightening, as are those of rawhide which is applied damp and shrinks on drying, or those which are tightened by wedges (Figure 15). Though lashings often offend the eye, they can be applied with esthetic intent and be an integral part of a work of art. Artistic lashings were regularly made in Micronesia and Polynesia on houses and small artifacts (Figure 16).

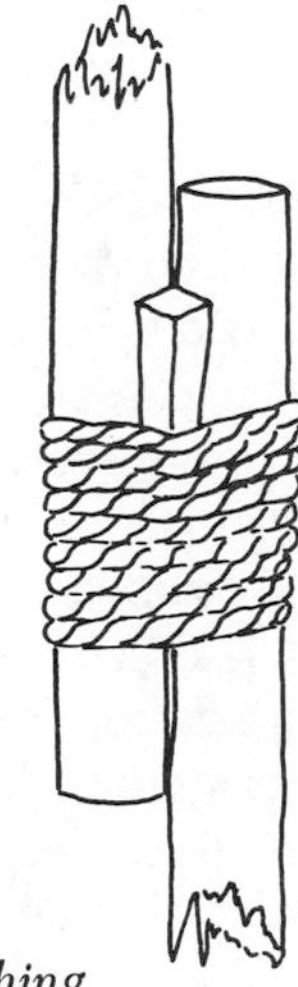

Figure 15

Wedge-tightened lashing

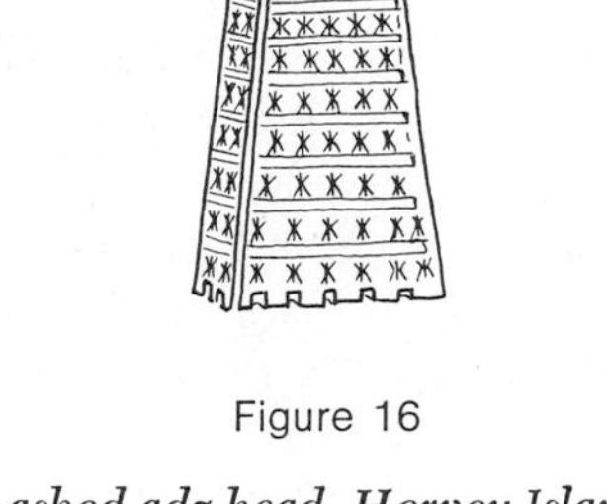

Figure 16

Lashed adz head, Hervey Islands

Lashings are the sole means of fastening substantial structures like buildings and watercraft. The plank boats of the Pacific Island world were fastened together with lashings. A major merit of this form of fastening was the ability of the boat hull and auxiliary parts to "work," that is, to move slightly relative to each other without breaking apart. Such flexibility made for a stronger, smoother-performing boat in the long run, but it also caused the boat to leak constantly while underway. In western Europe construction scaffolding is still made of lashed poles, and in Japan scaffolding is of lashed bamboo. Such scaffolding may reach up many stories. While this use of an ancient construction method may be considered anachronistic, the fact that these technologically-advanced peoples have seen no need to replace it with something more modern is a tribute to the method.

To consider pegs as the functional equivalents of nails is not wholly correct. Pegs do not force their way through between the grain fibers as do nails, but rather are driven into prepared (bored) holes in the wood. Therefore, their grip is different. They are used to resist shearing forces rather than forces of tension along their axes. Rarely were two pieces of wood pegged together; instead the peg was used in conjunction with a fitted joint which served to hold the pieces and limit their motion, as in a mortice-and-tenon or dovetail. The peg was installed so that, through its resistance to shear, the remaining freedom of movement was stopped.

The many varieties of primitive adhesives fell into two major classes: vegetable gums, resins, saps, and their derivatives; and animal glues, some related to sinew. Adhesives were often used in conjunction with other fastenings, particularly lashings. Sinew, which has some adhesive properties, is virtually a self-adhesive lashing. (Rawhide shares some of these properties.) These adhesives were rarely used to join wood or to strengthen wooden joints but were frequently used to attach some other material to wood, as feathers to an arrow shaft.

One-piece construction to avoid the use of fastenings does not preclude the making of objects with movable parts, as in ornamental carvings, such as a ball in a cage, by modern whittlers. Comparable items, some intended as spindles, were carved by European peasant shepherds. Larger works along the same lines are found in the one-piece stools of the Guiana Bush Negroes (see Figure 17). Though foresight must be coupled with skill when producing such things, in other respects they are not technically remarkable.

Self-holding construction involves refraining from removing something as often as it does adding anything; for example, the forked top of a piece of wood is retained and utilized to hold a crosspiece. The stub of a fork protruding downward (inverted from the orientation of growth) may be an excellent holddown on a stake, while a fork of three branches

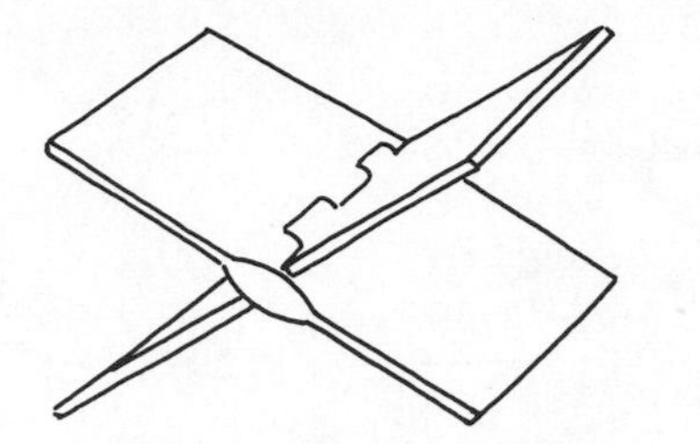

Figure 17

Guiana stool

provides a tripod. This approach to the use of materials is most fruitful when the materials are gathered with a specific use in mind, but the generic lumber-for-anything approach does not lead in this direction. Successful application means that the person doing the work is the best person to gather the raw materials for the job since he has its requirements and mode of execution most firmly in mind.

Technological advancement through time has seen the expansion of the materials roster, especially in the development of synthetic materials and the tendency toward generic, uniform materials. Because materials are as much a part of the technological complex as any other element, they have had a strong bearing on the end products.

7

Firemaking

Man's ability to make fire is almost as important as his ability to make tools. With tools, but without fire, culture would not have become at all elaborated.

Fire provides heat, light, and protection. It has also influenced diet, industry, and possibly human evolution. Cooking is a kind of predigestion which makes edible many foods which humans could not otherwise consume. As a softener and conditioner of foods, fire has probably played some role in mandibular and dental evolution. Its dietary influence is evident in the availability of fire- and smoke-dried foods out of season.

Fire-setting has altered the face of the earth and its flora, creating grasslands, deserts, second-growth forests, and destroying other environmental forms. Migratory cultivation, otherwise known as slash-and-burn, is heavily dependent on fire. Fire has also been invaluable in hunting — driving animals from cover, herding them to ambushes, and smoking them to stupefaction.

The industrial use of fire is equally extensive and important. Fire-hardened tips were used to arm spear shafts before stone points were affixed. In fact the earliest wooden artifact known, from the second interglacial episode of the Pleistocene Epoch in Europe, consists of fragments of such a fire-hardened spear. Heat was also used to aid in straightening projectile shafts. Neither true metallurgy nor the manufacture of ceramics could exist without the heat of fire. This list could be extended considerably without touching modern industrial uses of fire-derived heat.

Firemaking among nonliterate peoples usually follows one of two basic methods: friction or percussion.

Fire-by-friction is the method which most people associate with primitive peoples. This method was the first to be supplanted as other means were developed. If one may trust the proposition that very old cultural traits have many variant forms, then fire-by-friction must be very old, for there are many ways in which controlled friction can be generated. Friction devices fall into two classes: those relying on rotation (drills) and those relying on reciprocating motion (saws and plows).

The simplest of the fire drills is rotated between the palms of the operator. The drill rests on a prepared wooden hearth which may have a side-notched cavity to receive the drill's lower end. Adjacent to or below this cavity is the initial tinder supply. The operator briskly turns the drill by rubbing his palms together with the drill shaft between them. At the same time he applies as much downward pressure as possible. As his hands work down the shaft they are recovered to the upper end, and the drilling motion quickly continues. Given the right materials for drill, hearth, and tinder (and a bit of luck), the palm drill will produce a fire after about a minute of very hard work.

A substantial improvement in drilling fire came with the use of a bow drill. In this implement the drill shaft is steadied at the top by a socket or cap-piece which can also supply a downward pressure. The lower end of the shaft rests on a hearth similar to that used with the palm drill. Rotational force is applied to the shaft by means of a slack bow string wrapped once or twice around the shaft. The bow string is fastened to a light bow which is sawed back and forth to move the string and turn the drill shaft. In customary use the operator of the bow drill holds the cap in one hand and uses his other hand to work the bow; he may use one foot to hold the hearth steady. The quick action of the bow drill as a firemaking device is due in part to the increased pressure on the drill shaft which the cap makes possible and in part to the almost continuous rotation that keeps up the heat-producing friction.

The cap-piece of the bow drill may be varied into a mouthpiece which is held between the teeth, thereby freeing a hand for purposes other than steadying the drill shaft. This is especially useful when the bow drill is being used as a piercing drill rather than as a firemaker. (See Figure 4, page 31.)

The equally effective strap drill is a derivative of the bow drill and capitalizes on the potentialities of the cap-piece. In its simplest form the strap drill consists of a shaft, a steadying cap, and a strap or thong. The drill shaft is held by one operator while another operator pulls alternately on the ends of the strap which passes a turn or two around the shaft. It is basically a bow drill without the bow. Variations have two men operating the strap, or one man running the whole drill. In the latter instance the operator uses a mouthpiece instead of a hand-held cap and holds a strap end in each hand.

The pump drill offers another rotational method of making fire by friction. Basically it consists of a vertical shaft which passes loosely through a crosspiece positioned at right angles. Cords connect the ends of the crosspiece to the top of the shaft; their length is such that when they are taut the crosspiece is toward the lower part of the shaft. Commonly a flywheel or whorl is mounted on the shaft, usually toward its lower end, but occasionally at the extreme top. Initial rotation is imparted to the drill by turning the shaft with the fingers to wind up the cords, thereby raising the crosspiece. When the crosspiece is depressed it causes the cords to unwind and turn the shaft. As the crosspiece nears its lowest point pressure is lessened and continuing rotation of the shaft causes the cords to be wound in the opposite direction. The shaft then stops momentarily before new downward pressure on the crosspiece and another cycle. A rhythm of pumping is quickly established which can be maintained for some minutes without fatigue. The whole apparatus rests on a wooden hearth similar to that used with the other drills. (See Figure 6, page 32.)

The weight of the pump drill is significant in relation to its firemaking ability. Pressure of the shaft on the hearth is dependent upon weight and the intermittent pressure on the crosspiece. In lighter weights the pump drill is not an effective fire drill when compared to the bow or strap drills. It may, nonetheless, be preferred to the difficult palm drill.

When equipped with appropriate bits all of these fire drills may be used as well for more conventional drilling purposes as described in Chapter 5. Questions of priority of use, however, for piercing or for firemaking, must remain moot. Note that none of these devices is capable of continuous rotation in one direction but must reverse direction of rotation after a few revolutions. The stopping associated with this reversal allows a period of cooling which reduces effectiveness.

Reciprocating devices for fire-by-friction may be divided into two groups. The first group includes the fire saws in which a piece of wood, the "saw," is worked rapidly back and forth across a hearth. The hot, smoldering dust which is produced is permitted to fall on a tinder. The fire saw may be a complete apparatus, used for no other purpose, or it may be an artifact which has another purpose. An example for the first would be the Southeast Asiatic fire saw made of bamboo (Figure 18).

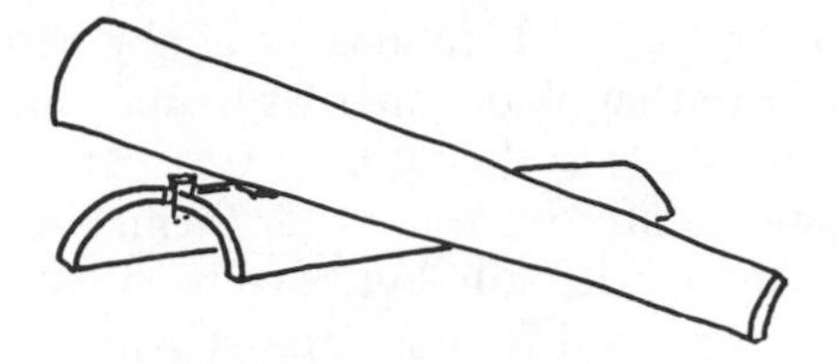

Figure 18

Bamboo fire saw

The saw is taken from a bamboo stalk of large diameter so that the blade is relatively straight in both directions, along the edge and from edge to back. The hearth is a hemicylinder of a smaller diameter which has been partly split. The hearth rests, concave side down, over the tinder and the crack of the split may be held open with a small wedge. The saw is worked across the crack to produce the glowing dust. A fire saw which is basically another artifact is that of the central Australian natives. They use a spear thrower, the edge of which is worked across an expedient hearth to make fire.

The fire thong or fire rattan is closely related to the fire saw in mode of operation. A long vegetable filament, often a strip of rattan, is held at both ends, drawn under tension beneath a suitable wooden hearth, and worked back and forth until the resulting friction produces a smoldering dust. A single operator manipulates the thong and holds the hearth down with one foot. (Despite the name of thong, leather is not used for the filament in this device.) Though the fire thong has an expedient air about it, the rattan is carried by some peoples in a pouch along with suitable tinder.

The fire saw and fire thong seem to lie, in speed and utility, between the palm drill and the bow or strap drill. They are probably faster in operation than the pump drill because more pressure may be applied.

The second reciprocating fire device is the fire plow, which takes the form of a hearth bearing a longitudinal groove and a stick which is the plow proper. The plow is worked back and forth in the groove until smoldering dust gathers at the ends of its track. The dust is then used to ignite a tinder. In use the hearth is held down by the feet of a squatting operator who thrusts the stick along the groove, applying most of the pressure on this push stroke. While the fire plow may be made as needed, the device has no other use; it does not represent, as do some fire saws, the expedient use of something with basically another purpose. In speed, however, it probably compares favorably with the fire saw.

Firemaking by percussion is the basis for the strike-a-light familiar from the American Colonial and Revolutionary periods. This approach has considerable antiquity, judging from its widespread application. Many items will spark when struck together; however, usually dissimilar pairs are more effective.

Among the materials used in varying combinations for fire by percussion are flint (and related stones), iron sulphide (pyrites), iron and steel, bamboo and pottery. In the northerly and southerly parts of the New World pyrites as well as flint and pyrites were used for firemaking. Flint and steel were European and Asiatic originally but have been widely diffused. Bamboo and pottery are reported from Southeast Asia and may, ultimately, depend on using porcelain rather than any high-fired ceramic. This could explain its area of distribution being restricted to the vicinity of China where porcelain originated.

The striking materials chosen were carried as a kit, together with a supply of tinder to catch the sparks. The kit, in gourd or pouch, was often as common an item of male accoutrement as are matches today.

Since all the percussion items were mechanically quite simple, it is surprising to find that they were confined mainly to advanced peoples. The inclusion of iron, steel, and porcelain is not, itself, sufficient reason for this restriction when one considers the general availability of the other materials.

In addition to the two basic firemaking methods — friction and percussion — outlined above, there is yet another which has intrigued investigators. As knowledge of the native peoples of Southeast Asia and Indonesia increased it became known, in the early nineteenth century, that they used a unique device, the fire piston (also known as the fire syringe and occasionally as the fire pump), which makes fire by compression of air (Figure 19).

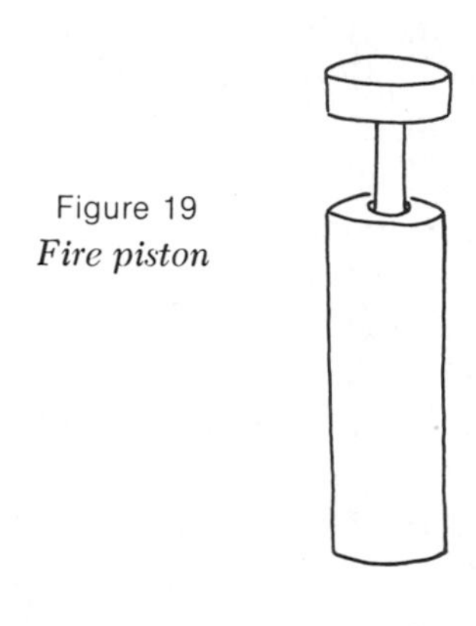

Figure 19
Fire piston

When gases are compressed heat is liberated. It is on this basis that most refrigeration cycles and the diesel engine work. In some fashion East Indians hit upon this principle and used it to make fire for domestic purposes. The basic device consists of a closed-end cylinder equipped with a tight-fitting piston. When the piston is driven sharply into the cylinder a tinder previously placed in the cylinder is ignited. The piston is withdrawn and the tinder is dumped out and fanned into a larger fire.

In brief the history of the fire piston has been reconstructed as follows. It was invented twice — early in the nineteenth century in Germany and in France. Both inventions were regarded as scientific toys though a later patent was secured in Britain with intent to supplant the strike-a-light. (The timing was poor for market development though, because the match had just been substantially improved.) When Europeans first became aware of the East Indian fire piston, it was assumed to have reached them through diffusion from Europe. Yet a number of factors point to a third invention in Asia.

First, the East Indians have been most inventive and eclectic in firemaking devices; there is hardly a method known anywhere in the world which is not found in Southeast Asia, also. Second, the fire piston was present in many variant forms and materials which implies a long acquaintance. Third, it is suggested that the fire piston was derived from the muzzle-loading cannon long known to the Indonesians. In support of this was the occasional occurrence of a false touch hole at the closed end of the cylinder. Finally, there was inadequate time between the known European inventions and the first evidences in the East for the device to have spread and become so widely diffused locally. A full review of the fire piston is to be found in the work of Balfour (1908).

Until the advent of the match firemaking was never very easy. It is understandable, then, that firekeeping and transporting should be significant aspects of the culture of fire. In most settled communities it was rarely necessary to make a fire from a cold start, for nearby could be found the smoldering remains of a fire — perhaps even several days old — which could be fanned into a blaze. Migratory peoples employed several means for carrying fires from camp to camp: a slow match or punk, consisting of a smoldering cord or pithy stalk; a firepot of gourd, coconut shell, or pottery; a torch, such as warmed Australian natives on cold days. In a canoe a sand box might carry a fire and furnish a cooking place en route as well.

Even when technical circumstances did not demand it, firemaking was sometimes practiced for ritual reasons. In the ceremonial cycle of some peoples it was customary to make new fires at certain times. All existing fires were extinguished and a priest or other leader performed a firemaking ritual. From this new fire the domestic fires of the group were rekindled. This is reported to have been the general custom among the Aztec and related peoples at the beginning of each new major calendric cycle. The renewal of fire at fifty-two-year intervals was accompanied by the renewal of other domestic items such as pottery.

It is probable that fire made on such ritual occasions is the product of archaic techniques of firemaking. Even though the match may have come into general use, one can still find at least the ritual pretence of having used a firedrill or other traditional method.

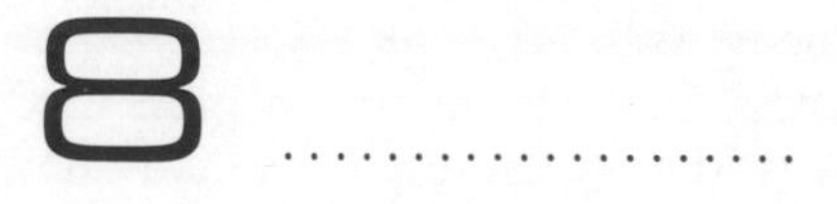

Stoneworking

Today, when it is difficult to think of a stone tool in modern use, one is hard pressed to comprehend that these tools held the center of the cultural stage for most of man's existence with a record of use extending two million years, according to potassium-argon dates from Olduvai Gorge in East Africa. Only with the close of the Neolithic period and the advent of the Metal Ages (of which the first was the Copper Age, also known as the Chalcolithic), did stone tools shift to a secondary status.

Stoneworking is a craft which many moderns consider truly representative of a crude technological state. Indeed, it may typify a simple technology but not one lacking in skilled manipulation. The production of a stone tool according to a preconceived pattern in the maker's culture is not an easy task. Further, the idea of chipping a stone to make a useful artifact is only obvious in restrospect. Harrison has stressed the major step involved in realizing that usable cutting edges could be produced by chipping stone (Harrison, 1930), a discovery which had consequences important to mankind for millions of years.

The stonework of the Paleolithic and Mesolithic periods were differentiated from that of the Neolithic by differences in the basic techniques employed. The Paleolithic and Mesolithic workers used various chipping techniques; the Neolithic peoples ground their stone tools into shape. Kroeber has observed that chipping took skill while grinding took foresight, but that, surprisingly, the skill was sooner come by than the foresight. He attributes this unexpected order of events to psychological differences hinging on more prompt gratification of desires. (Kroeber, 1948:629) For a long time the presence of ground stone tools was considered to be basic to the definition of the Neolithic Age.

Percussion Chipping

Percussion chipping, historically the earliest subtype, depended upon the detachment of flakes by a blow which was generated and delivered by a variety of methods. Most obvious among percussion methods was the use of a hammerstone held directly in the hand. (The hafting of tools generally was late in their history.) Probably equally early was the anvil, or block-on-block, method. This yields quite good, controlled results when the mass of stone being worked is large, a quarter-kilogram or more. The anvil method may, in fact, be the only effective one with very large nodules. The Abbé Breuil has suggested an elaboration of the method in which a moving block is suspended from a tripod to swing, pendulum-style, against the workpiece (Breuil, 1949:40).

Percussion of stone against stone causes shattering around the point of contact, an undesirable side effect, which can be reduced by use of a more resilient hammer. By the Middle Paleolithic Age the cylinder hammer (sometimes, "baton") method was in vogue. A cylindrical hammer of bone, antler, or hardwood was struck, side-on, against the workpiece in much the same fashion as a hammerstone would be. The same effect may be gained, and a different kind of precision added to the process, through the use of a punch (also sometimes termed a baton) interposed between the stone hammer and the workpiece. The punch not only softens the shock, thereby reducing shattering, but facilitates direction and pinpointing of the blow.

Examination of the end product may not distinguish the work of the cylinder hammer from that of the punch, but both can be separated from that of the stone hammer alone. Regardless of the method of chipping employed, the artifacts of the Middle Paleolithic show a confidence in ability and a refinement of technique which come only with experience and mastery of a subject.

An abstract discussion of the particulars of stone chipping is difficult, but some analysis can be made. Of prime importance is the striking platform on which the chipping blow is delivered, for its relation to the rest of the stone determines the results as much as any other factor. The angle which the platform bears to the long axis of the matrix (or core) and to the adjacent surface is fairly consistent for a given product in a given culture and may be caused either by a functionally-linked derivation or a culturally-dictated behavioral pattern.

The striking platform may exist simply on a functional basis, by definition the place at which the chipping blow is struck. In this usage all chipped stones possess striking platforms. However, a major advance in stone chipping came late in the Lower Paleolithic with preparation of a striking platform prior to release of the desired flake. One or more blows were struck to create a platform at the proper angle in the proper place. Then the main parting blow could be delivered with a higher probability of success. The unprepared or adventitious striking platform is a product of the situation and only peripherally cultural. The prepared striking platform, by contrast, is very much a cultural artifact, being made to a culturally-established standard. It is this latter type of platform which displays greater consistency as to type. Analysis of striking platforms has provided a key to some Paleolithic behavioral patterns.

The stones best adapted to chipping, as opposed to grinding, of tools are those which possess a "conchoidal" fracture. The scar of a chip removed is like the impression of a shell (particularly a clamshell or oystershell). Though not a stony substance, glass exemplifies well the conchoidal fracture which may be seen in the small chipping along any cut, unpolished edge. (Incidentally, glass makes an ideal material for chipped tools and was avidly sought by recent primitives over the world. For example, caches of broken glass were dumped along the central Australian telegraph lines to lessen pilferage of the crossarm insulators.) The conchoidal fracture is found in obsidian (volcanic glass), flints, jaspers and chalcedonies. All of these were commonly used when available. Other stones were, perforce, chipped into shape but did not yield such controlled or handsome results.

The bulb of percussion is a product of the shock wave creating the fracture. It is, in fact, a portion of a cone, fragmentary because the cone intersects the outer surface of the remaining matrix (core). The conical character of the bulb is evident in those cases where a pebble or a BB shot has struck a glass window pane. The resulting fracture may show a clean hole with a series of small radial cracks. On the side of the glass opposite that of the impact will be a conical (conchoidal) depression with its apex at the hole. The plug, probably shattered, from this cavity is the cone of percussion in this instance. The stone core or matrix from which a flake is struck shows the analogous depression. The mating surface of the flake shows the partial cone (or bulb) at the end nearest the striking platform (see Figure 20).

By the location of the bulb or its matching depression we may know where the separating blow was struck. Remains of the striking platform

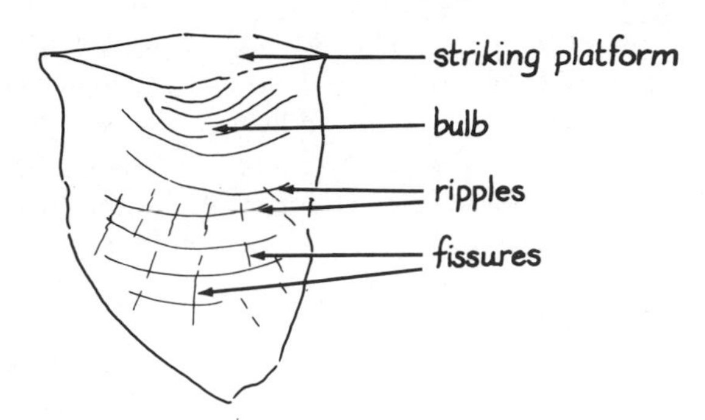

Figure 20

Diagnostic details of a flake

may have been removed from the flake end by later chipping. Together the platform and bulb add to our knowledge of past stoneworking technologies.

Radiating from the point of impact, and seen across the interface of flake and core, are a series of radial fissures which correspond to the radial cracks in the damaged window pane above. They, too, serve to guide us to the point of impact.

A part of the shell-like figure which suggested the conchoidal appellation is a series of concentric arcs or ripples about the impact point. These have often been likened to a "frozen" (stop-motion) representation of the ripples resulting when a stone is dropped into a still pond. The analogy is probably more than just a figure of speech; if the truth were known the ripples would likely be found at regular points, nodes or anti-nodes, in the wave system which the shock induced in the stone. The full circular pattern is truncated because the impact point is at one edge of the field. A better analogy would have the pond disturbed at some point along its edge. With the center of the ripples being at the impact point, we have a further clue to the latter's location.

Pressure Chipping

Historically stone chipping preceded stone grinding; and percussion chipping, discussed above, preceded pressure chipping.

The differences between percussion and pressure chipping revolve around the source of stress which produces the desired fracture. Both methods fracture stone by overloading it, one method quite abruptly, the other comparatively more gradually. Pressure can probably be increased by small increments, and the necessary level can be reached without fear of an unnecessary overload. Pressure chipping does not have the tendency toward shattering and offers control beyond that of the best percussion chipping.

In practice the pressure chipping tool, commonly an antler tine, a tapered wooden pin, a sharpened bone, or a hardwood fid, is pressed against the point to be chipped. With a sharp increase in pressure a flake is forced off. For simple pressure flaking the workpiece is held in one hand commonly protected by a leather pad, and the flaking tool is wielded by the other hand. At times the work-holding hand may be steadied or supported on a rest (for example, the knee on the same side). Occasionally the workpiece may be rested on the ground and held fast by the hand or feet.

Some analysts of prehistoric stoneworking, doubting that the unassisted hand could develop the pressure evidently requisite in some instances have hypothesized the use of an auxiliary crutch. The flaking tool was allegedly mounted in its tip and the crutch was thrust from the operator's shoulder. In this manner more weight could be brought to bear against the flaking tool and the workpiece. Possibly this method, which has been demonstrated experimentally, was used to drive off large flakes, but the writer is aware of no ethnographic parallel to this alleged practice. One would presume that it would have some survival to historic times along with other stoneworking methods. Likewise, despite the general perishability of nonlithic artifacts there ought to be some fragmentary remains of the alleged crutches recovered archeologically.

There are many technical details which can be observed in the analysis of stone chipping. Many of these form the basis of typologies, allegedly reflective of behavioral differences, cultural standards, and differing cultural traditions for tool manufacture. The reader is referred to the works of Sonnenfeld (1962), Semenov (1957), and Holmes (1919).

Stone Grinding

The grinding of stone into tools was a hallmark of the Neolithic Age. Today the importance of this technological advance has been subordinated. A major change in subsistence pattern, the shift in emphasis from food collection to food production, is now regarded as the basis for recognition of the Neolithic.

The advent of ground stone tools did not mean a total abandonment of chipping methods. Characteristically, this cultural change was as much supplementary as it was substitutive. In many cases the old (in this case, chipped stone tools) continued, virtually unaltered, alongside the new. This was especially true of chipping and grinding because tools were often given a rough shaping by chipping before the final shaping by grinding. The grinding process might be applied only to the cutting edges or other significant areas, leaving the marks of the preliminary chipping visible elsewhere.

As remarked above, grinding is a slower process than chipping. Most chipped stone artifacts can be produced in five to fifteen minutes of work, though an especially fancy piece, more artistic than utilitarian in purpose, could take several hours of careful work. Grinding has none of this speed; instead hours, days, or even weeks of work may be necessary, depending upon the method employed, the hardness of the stone, the amount of preliminary shaping, the artifact produced, and the degree of finish sought. One can indicate only the abstract order of difference in time between the two major approaches: for chipping the working time is measured in minutes, for grinding the working time is measured in days.

Extensive employment of the grinding method for stone shaping was perhaps impossible until the Neolithic improvement in subsistence had occurred and provided people with more time to devote to the task. In terms of energy expended the ground stone tools are much more expensive than chipped tools; however, like the even more expensive metal tools which superseded them the ground stone tools performed more efficiently in some tasks (Pope, 1923:56).

Stone grinding methods may be applied to a wide range of materials. Stones of conchoidal fracture may be ground into tool shapes; in later prehistoric times the working edges might be ground while general shaping was by chipping. Even-grained, laminar, and granular stones are not well adapted to controlled chipping but lend themselves well to grinding after a preliminary shaping by pecking, which abrades away small bits at each blow.

Drilling

Grinding methods are not only employed for general shaping and edge sharpening but are the basis for the drilling and sawing of stone. This basis has not changed radically to the present day: thin grinding wheels are customary for cutting brick, tile, and stone on construction jobs. Modern drilling does represent improvement with the availability of very hard drill materials and with the radically different approach of ultrasonic methods.

Primitive drilling of stone proceeds by two alternative methods: the use of a hard drill on a soft stone and the use of a soft drill on a hard stone. In the former instance the hard drill is often a chipped stone tool, like a slender projectile point, which is rotated in the hand or with a drilling device. Optimally such a drill should remove chips, but it will not remove a continuous shaving of stone. (Neither will any modern stone drill known to the author. Stone drilling is simply not like drilling wood or metal.) The drill usually tapers to a point, and the hole it makes shows a corresponding taper. Though shortness of the drill point may limit the depth of hole, depth may be increased by backdrilling. After the initial drill hole has reached its limit, a second hole is drilled from the opposite side of the workpiece to meet the first hole. Evidence of backdrilling may be found in occasional misalignment of the two bores. Backdrilling is also frequently shown in a double taper of the resulting hole, the smallest diameter being found at the intersection of the two bores.

The use of a soft drill to pierce a hard material by grinding involves an abrasive which does the actual cutting. The drill bit carries the abrasive to the seat of operations and determines the diameter of the hole. Soft materials cannot be pierced by this grinding method, which is effective only on hard materials that resist the grinding action with resultant wear.

Solid or tubular soft drill bits may be used. The solid bit is simpler to produce and use but is much slower, especially in larger diameters. The solid bit must remove a cylinder of material equal to the diameter of the hole times the thickness of the material. The tubular or hollow drill removes a similar cylinder's outer volume minus the volume of the plug left inside the tube. The drilling interface of the tubular drill is a ring rather than the disc interface of the solid drill.

The ability of all soft drills to embed and carry the abrasive is closely linked to progress of the work. Sometimes the end of the drill is roughened or slotted to retain the abrasive. In quite sophisticated forms the abrasive may be incorporated into the body of the drill, as in diamond-dust drills.

Primitive practice saw solid drillbits of stick, bone, and antler, with markedly hollow bones (bird bones) and cane or reed used for tubular drills. Some American Indians used rolled sheet metal tubes for hollow bits. Among the wide variety of abrasives quartz sand is a natural, fast-cutting abrasive readily available.

Backdrilling was sometimes employed with soft drills, most commonly with tubular forms. After drilling from both sides had progressed to a point, the worker might punch out the remaining core or plug. If this were done after some backdrilling there would be less chance of splintering out one surface of the workpiece or having unwanted fractures occur. Evidence of backdrilling in this procedure would be a hole smooth at both ends with a rough area (that of the fracture) midway through. Of course, final smoothing of the hole or use-induced wear could obliterate this roughness.

Sawing

The sawing of stone is another grinding process. It is performed with a typically toothless saw which is itself abrasive or carries an abrasive in the fashion of a soft drill. The grinding effect is along a line and eventually wears its way through. Primitive saws for stone were usually another, laminar, stone such as slate which, in conjunction with an abrasive paste, could work through very hard materials.

The capacity of the aboriginal stone saw for deep cuts was limited by the tendency for the blades to be thick and to have a wedge-shaped, rather than parallel-sided, cross-section. The blades were not very deep and wore off as they were used. It should be noted that stone sawing proceeds uniformly from the plane of one surface to that of the other, not from one edge to the other. The direction of work is conditioned by the nature of the saw blade, the process of back sawing, and the possibility of a controlled fracture.

The slowness of stone grinding, drilling, and sawing led to shortcut techniques like backsawing to shorten the sawing process. When the remaining web of stone had been ground adequately thin, it was broken in two. Although the rough area of the fracture has been found in some semifinished pieces, it is more likely to be ground smooth than is the corresponding area inside a hole.

Stone grinding techniques have not been subjected to as much intense analysis as have stone chipping techniques. Only the grossest of technical differences are used as the basis for typological distinctions. This topic is one which certainly has not been overworked by prehistorians or historians of technology.

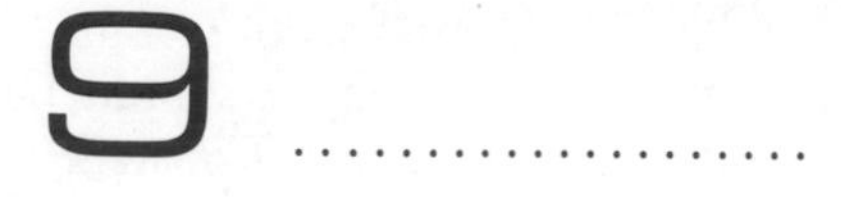

Woodworking

Wooden artifacts are probably as old as any human products, but our knowledge of them is limited by the archeological record. Under any but optimum conditions wood perishes soon and leaves little trace of its existence. It is, therefore, not surprising to learn that the oldest wooden artifact known is a fire-hardened spear from the Middle Pleistocene (Movius, 1950; Oakley, 1950). Only much later, in the Mesolithic of northern Europe, are there substantial evidences of the range of uses to which man has put wood (Clark, 1952).

The approach to wood among people of simpler technologies differs substantially from that of twentieth-century Westerners. The primitive worker is much closer to the entire process by which wood is converted to a finished product. The craftsman himself may cut the tree or designate the tree to be cut, may reduce the tree to the pieces he needs, and is likely to perform all operations from the rough shaping of the object to its finishing.

The primitive woodworker will usually select the individual tree, branch, or root which best suits his needs because it already approximates the outlines of the desired finished product and can be worked into final shape with a minimum of effort. A primitive woodworker often can select wood which meets his other desiderata as well. In most modern circumstances, however, one must be content with lumber which meets general specifications. The modern woodworker is usually unable to operate in a particularistic manner. He must, instead, use generalized materials to create, through synthetic means, the desired characteristics in his wood.

The two approaches, ancient and modern, can be contrasted by saying that the primitive woodworker takes apart as little as possible when he makes something so that he not be called upon to put it together again, whereas the modern woodworker dismantles the wood of his basic supply and then reassembles it in a manner to suit himself but which may be quite far from nature. A direct reflection of this contrast may be found in the presence of the modern lumberyard stocked with wood cut to standard sizes that bear a general, but not particular, relevance to their ultimate use.

Primitive peoples may fell trees by any method save chopping. As a preliminary the tree may be killed before it is needed by belting (removal of the bark and cambium layer). This makes it easier to bring the tree down later by controlled burning. Successive burning sessions may be alternated with scraping away the charred wood. Chopping was a last resort until the advent of metal axes made it somewhat easier.

The felled tree may be reduced to manageable size by splitting and cutting it into lengths. If the whole trunk is desired intact, a large trunk-moving party is summoned to man-handle the trunk from the forest to a stream or workplace. Water transport was, for most primitives, the easiest way to move logs. With a small effort the logs would float along either singly or fastened into rafts. A few heavy hardwoods, however, like teak, had to be rafted with other, lighter woods.

Reducing

Though an effort may be made to use a piece of wood as it was cut in the forest, most logs have to be reduced to smaller pieces of wood either by sawing (in more modern times) or by splitting (in earlier times). Splitting logs involved the use of wedges of wood or antler driven into a crack or a check to force off a portion of the log. Tractable grain patterns in wood made it possible to split off a succession of parallel-sided planks (see Figure 21).

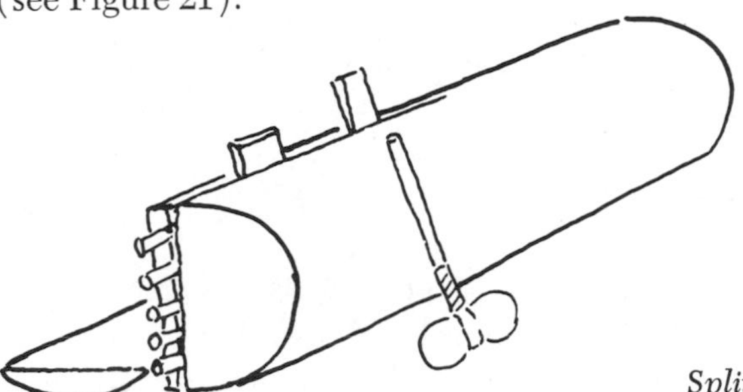

Figure 21

Splitting planks by wedging

Important adjuncts for man in the provision of smooth-surfaced planks and timbers were the adz, a widely useful early tool employed among technologically simpler peoples, and the Western broad ax which became important during the Middle Ages. The nature of the broad ax and the manner of its use made it more applicable to timbers than to planks.

Reduction of logs by sawing became important in western Europe only in the last millenium. In the fourteenth century reciprocating saws were powered by watermills and somewhat later by windmills, but hand sawing remained important up to the twentieth century in some parts of the world.

The hand sawing of planks is usually called pit sawing, though an actual pit may not be involved. If a pit is used, the upper edges of the pit side (especially the long sides) were finished with logs or dressed timbers to support the work and reduce crumbling. Movable crosspieces, resting on the side timbers, supported the log being sawn. Several of these could be shifted along to support the cut and uncut portions without being cut through by the advancing saw (see Figure 22). If a true pit were not dug due to the brief span of its proposed use, the hardness of the ground, a high water table, or the habits of the culture, elevated trestles or an X-shaped horse or buck were used. Found in areas of European influence, the trestles, built like the bents of a bridge, rested on stringers

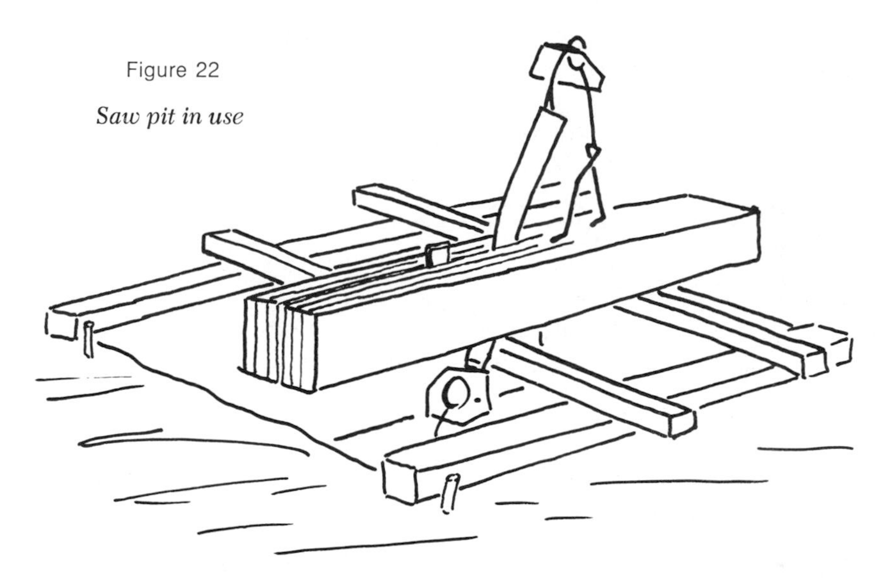

Figure 22

Saw pit in use

in the ground and held the log being sawed (Figure 23). The X-shaped support, common in the Far East, was often located so that one-third of the log projected beyond it with the remainder serving as a counterbalance. Stability might be given the X-frame by having a third struc-

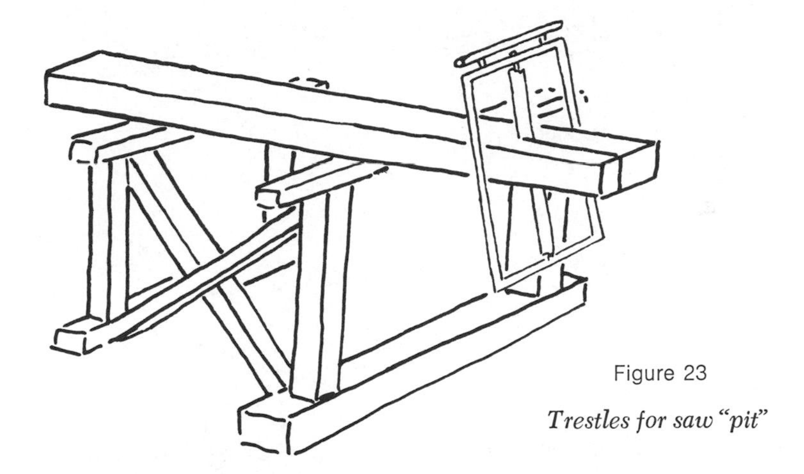

Figure 23

Trestles for saw "pit"

tural member reach from the crossing to the ground to form an asymmetrical tripod with an upward-protruding fork.

The saws employed for pit sawing fell into two major classes: the free-bladed saw and the framed saw. The free-bladed saw had a tiller-like projection from its upper end with a cross handle and a second cross handle which could be fastened to the lower end. The lower handle was necessarily removable in order that the blade would be drawn out through the cut. The framed blade was mounted on the midline of a rectangular frame with the plane of the blade at right angles to the plane of the frame. The frame spanned the entire log being sawed and was demountable so that the blade could be freed and drawn out through the cut. The end pieces of the blade were held in devices which, through the use of wedges or screws, applied a tension to the blade. A variant form of a framed saw had the blade mounted on one side, a central longitudinal frame member, and a tensioning device. (See Figure 24.)

The motor habit patterns associated with the use of pit saws are reflected in the directions in which the saws cut. The free-bladed pit saw has its teeth raked from the main handle toward the tip with its removable handle. In this regard it looks like a push tool, but practice actually makes it a pull tool. The "pit man," beneath the log, provides the bulk of the cutting power as he pulls downward on the saw; the top man, standing on the log or a support plank, does little more than return the saw for another downward stroke. The lower position is, of course, the less enviable one because the man is showered with sawdust, does the bulk of the work, and may be standing in water or roasted by the sun.

An interesting variation of these habits is reported from China, a region dominated by the use of hand pull tools. Their framed pit saw has the teeth raking from the center toward each end of the blade. In this fashion the saw is a pull saw for each sawyer in the last half of his pull stroke and

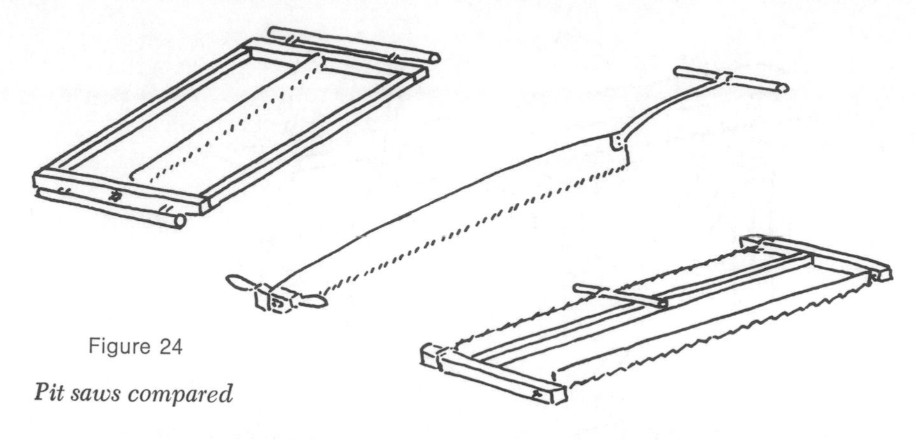

Figure 24

Pit saws compared

the top man is called upon to do his full share rather than place the bulk of the burden on his partner below. Because Far Eastern "pit" sawyers use a buck or horse to support their log, the work proceeds with the saw in a more horizontal position than with a true pit. This may be a factor in the rake of teeth, the posture of the sawyers, and the division of work between them (Hommel, 1937:227).

The modern saws — the circular saws and band saws — are of the last two centuries. The former came into prominence with the development of mass multiple manufacture of pulley blocks for the British Navy and merchant marine. The large band saw, a strictly twentieth-century version, capable of handling logs well beyond the capacity of the largest circular saws, has expanded the working horizons of the lumber industry. Both these modern saws depend on power from nonhuman and nonanimal sources, such as wind, water, and steam.

Shaping

Rough shaping was carried on with ax, adz, chisel, fire, and hot water or steam. The work of shaping was reduced as much as possible by choosing materials whose original form was close to that of the object desired or by modifying the growth of the material to approximate the finished object.

In skilled hands an ax can be used for a variety of purposes; however, in rough shaping its use might be confined to the cross-cutting of wood where today we might employ a saw. This limited use coordinates well with the use of the adz for hollowing and smoothing. The broad ax, used mostly for rough hewing along the grain of the wood, was a companion tool of the adz in preindustrial Europe, but it is lacking among more primitive peoples. Though the chisel is less widespread than either ax or adz, it is not confined to more complex cultures.

Fire in the form of controlled burning was often employed for rough shaping. Burning sticks might be placed against a log which was to be severed, while adjacent parts of the log were dampened to limit the fire. The log itself might be set afire without the use of auxiliary brands. The charred area was periodically scraped or bruised away in order to expose a fresh surface for burning. Though slow, this process is less laborious than hewing away with crude implements and could be superintended by unskilled workers.

Bending wood to shape was more commonly practiced by primitive peoples than by technicians today. Unseasoned ("green") wood was drawn into shape and held there by temporary means until it dried, or it was held permanently by elements of the structure. The frequent occurrence of this shaping method among primitives is attributed to their closeness to sources of raw material. It would be comparatively difficult for the Western carpenter to lay his hands on such unseasoned wood.

Working green woods without bending is also common. Certain woods, like American sycamore or Hawaiian koa, which become very hard or tough when quite dry are difficult to work with ordinary tools. Indeed, the modern craftsman, if he tries them at all, may employ techniques suited to metals of middling hardness.

If dry materials must be bent, moisture is often added to make them pliable, as in basketry, when strands are soaked before use. Hot water or steam (at atmospheric pressure) is even more effective than cold water. The Indians of the Pacific Northwest Coast of North America made bentwood boxes and other containers by kerfing and bending unseasoned red cedar planks. The steam and hot water employed were generated in a trench floored with hot stones covered with seaweed. Dampened moss was packed on the points where bends were to be made, and overnight steaming was customary.

Too large to be treated in a trench, the Northwest Coast dugout canoe, in addition to being excavated inside by cutting and burning, might be expanded in beam by bending the sides outward. Water in the excavated hull was heated by immersion of group after group of fire-heated stones (the basic process is known as "stone boiling" and was used to cook in inflammable containers such as baskets). When the sides of the canoe were softened adequately, they were forced apart and held in position by driving thwarts between them. These thwarts remained as permanent parts of the finished canoe and prevented reversion to original shape when the canoe was softened by soaking while in service.

Heat alone was usable for bending some materials. The California Indians drew arrowshafts over grooves in heated soapstones (which does not pop and spall when hot) to straighten them, thus operating on exactly the same principles as bending. Glowing coals or heated stones provided radiant heat for bending bamboo, which is treated more readily by exposure to heat than by soaking or steaming.

Finishing

Surface finishing of products may not occur, since the marks of rough shaping may form a desirable textured pattern and so be allowed to remain. If this "finish" is planned, the rough work may progress in a neater, more orderly fashion, with even tool strokes carefully distributed over the surface treated. Though this kind of finish leads to a better grade of rough work, the overall effort of manufacture is probably not diminished. The effort is simply concentrated on one major step along the way.

If archeological interpretations are correct, scrapers have been used since virtually the beginning of stone tools, but few of the earliest forms show a design especially for woodworking. The same scrapers may have been used in hide dressing as well. It may be noted, though, that refined analysis of edge wear will probably differentiate between these kinds of use when applied on a wider scale than the few instances to date (Semenov, 1957; Keller, 1966). Metal and glass scrapers came late in technological history; the latter material was particularly favored by fine cabinetmakers because it was easily kept very sharp.

True primitives probably used few other tools for smoothing, but they did use some abrasive materials which approximate modern sandpaper. Many peoples of the Pacific world used sharkskin as an abrasive film. The scouring rush (*Equisetum*), which has a high silica content, was used in both Old and New Worlds. Doubtless there were other plants of the same general nature.

Beginning with the Romans, the plane and the spokeshave have been used for finishing flat and curved surfaces. The plane, with metal body and blade, is at least two thousand years old, having been reported archeologically from Italy and Roman Britain. However, the advanced form from this early date seems to have disappeared during the Dark Ages in Europe. The next planes were substantially simpler forms with wooden bodies and metal blades. Changes were minor and modest until the nineteenth century when metal blade-holding and blade-adjusting mechanisms appeared, and the wooden bodies were supplanted by cast metal bodies. There was a brief efflorescence of elaborate, specialized forms, such as the circle plane and the router plane, most of which are only dimly remembered today. Machines, either hand-held or bench-mounted, have driven them out of common use.

The spokeshave has a history which in recent histories parallels that of the plane and includes a design change in its most recent forms. The early spokeshave had a blade ending in tangs bent at right angles to the plane of the blade. These tangs passed through the handle and held the blade at a fixed distance from the sole of the tool. The space between blade and sole formed a sort of throat through which passed the shaving being cut off the workpiece. The space in this throat limited the depth of cut, for too thick a shaving would not pass through and the tool was choked to a stop until a lighter cut was made. This type of tool had a steel blade and wooden handle. (See Figure 11, Chapter 5). The more recent spokeshave was much like a miniature plane with large lateral handles. The blade projected below a sole, and the amount of projection controlled the depth of cut. The shaving passed upward through the body of the tool by way of a throat at the blade, in the same manner as in a plane. This plane-like form persists, and the earlier spokeshave is made by only a few firms which maintain production of traditional types.

The prehistoric spokeshave, first recognized in the European Upper Paleolithic period, was a blade (prismatic flake) base which was deeply side-notched. This "strangulated" blade has been interpreted as being for the smoothing of round shafts. Again a detailed analysis of edge wear might confirm or deny that the tool was used on wood.

The development of the spokeshave from a simple concave scraper, through the stirrup form of the free-standing blade, to the plane-like type illustrates a trend noticeable in many kinds of tools and work situations. Each of these tools is progressively self-controlling in depth of cut and less dependent upon the skill of the user. Machine tools have especially usurped from the craftsman (read "operator") that element of skill, delicacy of touch, and judgment which came from substantial experience with tools, materials, and a class of products.

Of the use of paints and varnishes for wood finishing we have no knowledge of great prehistoric depth. At best one may hazard the opinion that the earlier and simpler primitive peoples applied some stains to their wooden products. Superficial burning, incising, carving, and the addition of ornamental studs are all noted among nonliterates, as among West Africans and Congolese.

Fastening

Fastenings for wood and other materials have become numerous and sophisticated in modern times. With these devices and adhesives almost any kind of joint between diverse materials can be made and is likely to prove durable. Perhaps the proliferation of fastenings is yet another indicator of technological complexity.

Many earlier peoples met their fastening problems by avoiding the issue entirely; they made their products out of one piece of material. Thus, a hay fork was cut from a small tree or tree branch which naturally divided in a suitable fashion. The main stem formed the handle, and lesser branches, cut to length, formed the tines, eliminating the need to attach tines to a separate handle. This approach in the making of artifacts is most feasible when one craftsman carries the job from the acquisition of raw materials to the finished product, since he can best select in the forest the branch he needs.

Making objects of one piece does not preclude their having movable parts. Sometimes the manufacture of items with articulated pieces from a single original piece was a tour de force by the craftsman, and sometimes it was simply an answer to a common problem. Some forms of pliers-like wooden tongs, used in the preindustrial Netherlands to pull up thistles, were made from one piece but were necessarily movable. A one-piece, X-shaped, folding, wooden stool is reported from the Guianas (Dark, 1954:33). (See Figure 17, Chapter 6.) A laminated version of this stool is now made in Honduras for sale to tourists (Clifton, 1969).

The weight of wooden parts themselves or the weight of something which they support might hold the ensemble together. This principle was used when a beam rested in a forked support. Weight also holds together many a tripod-like device. Parts of weighted beam traps and of water-lifting sweeps (the Egyptian *shadouf*) are articulated on this basis (see Figure 25).

Figure 25

Shadouf *for water lifting*

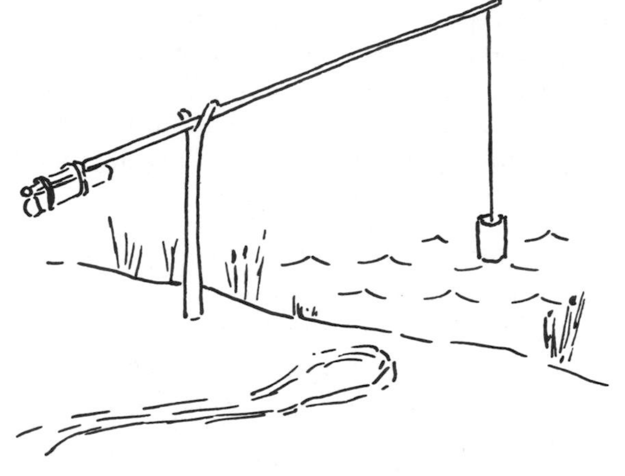

Most early fastenings were nonmetallic because either the use of metals still lay in the future or the metals present were in short supply. Consequently other techniques and materials were used instead: cutting and fitting joints (some self-fastening), sewing and lashing, and adhesives.

The provision of closely fitted joints in woodworking seems positively correlated with available time and craftsman's skill and negatively correlated with advancing fastening technology. The use of mortise-and-tenon, dovetail, rabbet, and stepped scarph joints diminishes with the modern rise of lapped or butted joints coupled to capable metal fittings and modern adhesives. However, it should be noted that elaborately fitted joints do depend, in a measure, on good tools. Surely it is no accident that woodworking reached a high level of sophistication in aboriginal western

Africa where there also existed a prehistoric iron metallurgy to provide fine tools. The woodwork of New Zealand (Maori), the New Guinea area (the northern and eastern Melanesians), and the Pacific Northwest Coast (Tlingit to Nootka) may have owed a great deal to ground stone tools in various "greenstones," jades, jadeite, and nephrite.

Some few joints possessed substantial holding power without auxiliary fastening by cross pegs. The woods and their grain were so selected as to tighten upon seasoning and shrinking. Pegging by itself, however, was no direct fastening for pieces not otherwise fitted together. The closest approach to a direct fastening came with the use of dowels, but these were often augmented by an adhesive.

Sewing, the repetitive passing of a cord *through* the pieces of wood to be joined, and lashing, the repetitive passing of a cord *around* the pieces to be joined, were both commonly used. The suggestion that wood may be sewn frequently evokes a surprised reaction, but the technique was rather commonly applied by primitive peoples. The sewing cord was passed through holes made by an awl or drill; it did not follow a needle which had forced the openings. Sewing closed the final corner of a Pacific Northwest Coast bentwood box (Figure 26), fastened the planks of a Pacific islands planked canoe, and was used in Iron Age western Europe to fasten boat planks. The stitches were sometimes concealed ("blind") so as to be invisible from the outside of the box or vessel; at other times they formed a regular, decorative pattern.

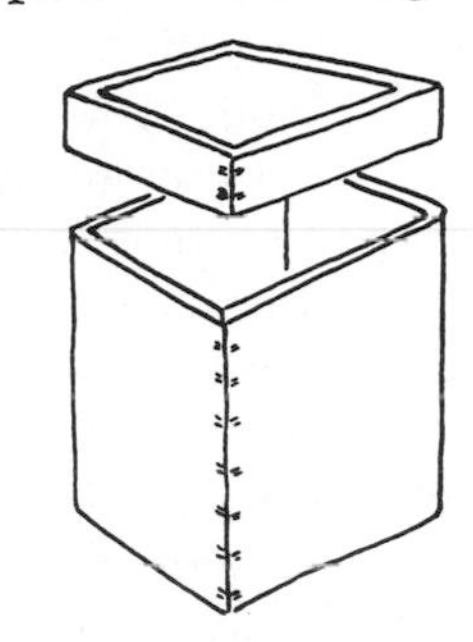

Figure 26
Sewn corner of Pacific Northwest bentwood box

Very common among nonliterates was the lashing of wood to wood and of other materials to wood, as in the lashing of a stone projectile point to its wooden shaft. Pacific island house frames were lashed together, sometimes with great care taken to produce an ornamental effect. The Eskimo made extensive use of lashings on sleds and skin-covered boats (the kayaks and umiaks). Many temporary structures in northwestern Europe and in Japan were lashed together, such as the scaffolding on buildings under construction or repair.

Lashings lend themselves very well to fastening woody materials which will not hold pegs, nails, or screws. Rushes and bamboo, being very soft and very hard, respectively, are often lashed. The Marsh Arabs of Iraq make elaborate structures of bundles of reeds lashed together. In this fashion they manage to overcome a general absence of wood. Bamboo tends to crack when anything is driven into it without a pilot hole being drilled beforehand; consequently, bamboo structures such as Southeast Asiatic houses or Japanese scaffolding are lashed together.

Finally, lashing and sewing produce a flexible joint, providing the structure with a degree of flexibility which permits it to give under stress without coming apart. This same character of yielding makes a basket a strong container for a given weight; a rigid container would need to be far heavier to withstand the same stress. Flexibility accounts, in part, for the seaworthiness of the Oceanic outrigger canoe, held together — planks, outriggers, and all — by lashings and stitching.

Adhesives were not used very much by nonliterate peoples to join woody materials. Perhaps the reason lies with the large quantity of glue needed for any sizable job and the circumstance that virtually all the older glues were water soluble. The first condition would limit the extent of use and the other would restrict the types of service. (Only in very recent times have we in the West made great use of glues on wood, adhesives which are a far cry from those of the past.) In addition, methods other than glue could join larger items more permanently.

Adhesives were usually called into service to fasten other materials to wood. Gums and resins were more widely used than asphaltum, probably because they occur more widely. Rawhide and sinew lashings, both applied when damp, have some adhesive properties. The attachment of arrowheads in many cultures furnishes instances of the use of sinew. Feathers can be fastened with an adhesive alone. The stone knife on a central Australian spear thrower is held in place with a gummy substance.

Metallic fastenings were in short supply until very recently. Though they have been used in the Western world, since Bronze Age times, they have been sporadic in occurrence and usually confined to luxury products. The furnishings of a Dynastic Egyptian queen might be nailed but hardly those of one of her subjects. Generally, metal fastenings were used when nothing else would suffice or when exceptional strength was needed.

Salvage of metal fastenings from discarded items was standard practice. Old buildings were burned and the ashes sifted for the nails. Hulls of worn-out wooden ships were burned on the beach in order to retrieve the metal they contained. Scrap metal was reforged directly into new products rather than being resmelted in a mixture with fresh ore. In this fashion the metal was recycled through the technology until it was reduced to tiny pieces or was lost through mischance.

Finally, though some metal fastenings were applied for ornamental as well as utilitarian reasons, there were others whose purpose was solely ornamental. African craftsmen studded the handles of tools with ornamental brass-headed nails and similar items when they were available.

10

Basketry

Basketry comprises techniques by which relatively stiff elements are interwoven or intertwined to produce containers and plane objects. Basketry differs from some other textile techniques in that its products are usually made freehand, rather than on a frame or loom. Mason defined basketry as "a textile art without machinery" (Mason, 1904, subtitle). Whatever the problems of definition, and they are many, rarely is there any practical confusion over what is a basketry object and what is not. Similarly the distinctions between baskets and mats are vexatious in theory but far simpler in practice.

The prehistory and history of basketry are rather vague due to the perishable nature of the material employed. In most circumstances, because of seasonal fluctuations in soil moisture, basketry has not been preserved. However, the dry caves of the American Southwest and the bogs of Denmark have yielded up perfectly preserved specimens. Nearly all peoples of the world had basketry at the time of their discovery by Westerners; those that did not at least knew about basketry in other cultures. Though early concrete examples of baskets come from Mesolithic times, one may guess that they had their roots in the late Paleolithic.

The attention of scholars interested in this subject has been focused on typologies of manufacturing techniques rather than on products. Though each writer has drawn on the contributions of others, each has emerged eventually with a unique scheme. Some of these typologies have been made quite elaborate in order to cover the topic comprehensively while reflecting nuances in technique. This discussion, however, will be based on the simple classification of Mason in which he differentiated coiled from woven basketry (Mason, 1904:190). Expansions of segments will be provided as needed.

Coiled Basketry

Coiled basketry is formed from two basic elements: a foundation (of varying composition) which is turned or coiled upon itself in a helical and/or spiral fashion and the stitching or sewing which holds the foundation in this coiled position. The foundation is augmented in length as it is wound on itself, and the stitching proceeds as the winding is done to secure each increment to the foundation already sewn. Subtypes of coiled basketry are usually differentiated on the basis of variations in the foundation and in the stitching.

Foundations. Foundations for coiled baskets have been placed in three categories: vertical, triangular, and multiple. The names are deceptive because they do not appear to follow one consistent criterion of differentiation. The vertical foundation has a series of discrete rods placed one above another. (A one-rod foundation is included here despite obvious difficulties in fitting it to the foregoing statement!) Two-, three-, or four-rod foundations may be used or the rod itself may be replaced by a slat or a bundle of grasses (Figure 27).

The triangular foundation is usually of three rods placed at the vertices of an equilateral triangle. To expand the triangle would call for six rods and create undue complications. A bundle of grasses can replace the upper vertex of the triangle. In designating the number of foundation elements, one specifies the number added in each round of foundation, not the number enclosed in a given loop of stitching. The stitching may include more or less of the added material and always encompasses some of the previous round of foundation.

The multiple foundation (grass bundle) consists of elements too numerous and variable in number to enumerate. Commonly the bundle is of a larger diameter than a rod, though not necessarily larger than a group of rods. Baskets constructed on multiple foundations usually lack the gaps in their walls which are caused by irregularities in foundation rods; the bundle is pliant enough to fill in the spaces.

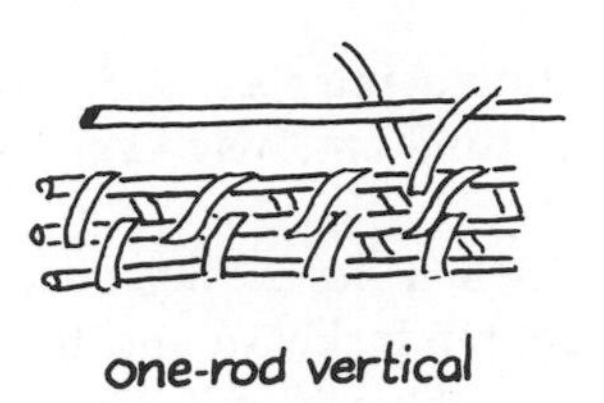

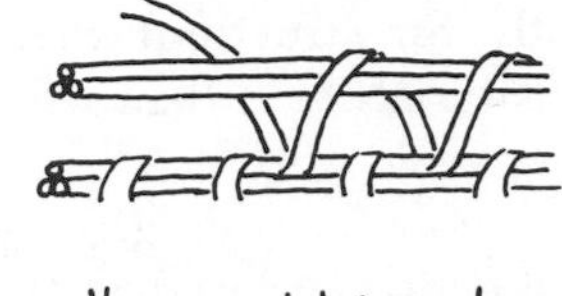

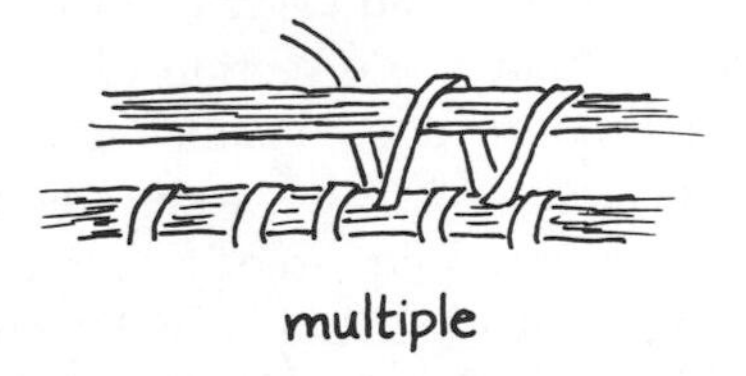

Figure 27

Coiled basketry foundations

Stitching. The stitching of basketry is another basis for classification. Though "sewing" is sometimes used as a synonym, stitching does not proceed with a needle and thread. Instead an awl is used to pierce a hole. The awl is withdrawn, and the sewing material is passed through the hole. Then the fiber is pulled tight with the fingers.

The awl itself is important to this process. Bone awls were often made from the leg bone of a large bird or small animal. The tip was cut and ground at an acute angle, and the condyles were retained to form a knob or grip at the upper end. The basket weaver could hold the awl in the hand between uses by palming the knob and passing the shaft of the short awl between the index and middle fingers or the middle and third fingers. This left the thumb and the index finger free to hold, direct, and pull on the stitching fiber.

Stitches on baskets are differentiated on the basis of interlock. Those which do not interlock pass around all or part of the foundation, but do not pass through the loop formed by another stitch. The interlocking stitches also pass around foundation elements, but in addition they pass *through* loops formed by previous stitches. An obvious distinction in result is that the interlocking stitches retain some integrity when the foundation elements are pulled out. A basket with noninterlocking stitches would separate into two parts if one round of foundation coils were removed.

Stitch splitting is another differentiating feature. Each stitch may enter and emerge from the body of the basket so that it passes between previous stitches. Or, the stitching material may pass through the material of a previous stitch on one surface of the basket or on the other or on both. When stitch splitting occurs there automatically exists an interlocking condition, but an interlock may occur in the absence of splitting. Splitting as a significant feature is noted only when it occurs regularly and recurrently for structural strength or decorative purposes. Broad, flat, sewing materials lend themselves to stitch splitting and may even make it difficult to avoid.

The direction of coiling is regularly noted when describing coiled basketry. Direction is stated as clockwise or counterclockwise and is viewed from the concave side of the basket, that is, looking into it. In the case of a plaque or flat tray, the viewing side would be the ornamented or finished surface. It has been observed that the direction of coiling is a culturally patterned feature, not a random one. Whole areas or time periods, speaking ethnographically or archeologically, were characterized by work in one direction. Presumably this can be directly correlated with earlier remarks about the patterning of work habits which were transmitted in cultural learning as readily as other technical details of the craft.

Compared to the elements used in weaving those used in basketry are limited and finite in length. New pieces must be added frequently to both foundation and stitching. With the single rod foundation the ends of old and new rods are tapered and overlapped under a number of sewing stitches; no tieing or adhesive is needed. With foundations of several rods, one is extended at a time with the joints staggered at various places around the basket's circumference. In multiple foundations many extensions are required, and these are staggered without much planning.

The stitching of a basket is executed so as to produce a regular pattern on the portion which shows. The spacing between stitches and their number are related to the distance around the circumference. When the diameter of the coil is expanded or contracted to produce changes in the contour of the basket, then the number of stitches or their spacing must be altered. In good quality work the extra stitches will be worked in at regular intervals or the number of stitches reduced by omissions at regular intervals. If the change in diameter is virtually continuous, as in a globular shape, then the changes will become a regular feature of the stitch pattern.

New stitching material must be added from time to time and is usually put in without knotting the ends. A new stitch strand is started with a turn or so of overlap with the old stitch so as to hold down the end of the latter. The end of the newly started strand is allowed to protrude until the basket is trimmed in the final finishing stages.

A coiled basket is usually started with a small spiral formed by the tightly coiled foundation sewn against itself. Only a few of the regular foundation elements are incorporated at this stage. Other forms of coiled basketry starts are basically rectangular, with either a back and forth meander of the sewed foundation before a circumferential pattern is begun or a laterally flattened or squared-off spiral before the beginning of the circumferential pattern which ultimately develops into the helical-spiral of the basket wall.

The top of a coiled basket may be finished by simply tapering off the foundation while stitching it down to the preceding round of foundation. The stitches around the top may be augmented or increased in frequency (closer together) to strengthen the edge. A separate round of a heavy withe may be stitched to the last round of true foundation to make a pronounced rim. The edge of a coiled basket, however, is usually plainer than that of a woven basket.

Ornamentation. If coiled baskets are ornamented or patterned it is usually by changes in the stitching. The foundation may be completely concealed or partly revealed, but it is rarely prominent enough to be an important esthetic element. At a simple level the stitching pattern may be changed on different parts of the basket — the stitches set more tightly, or omitted, or split, and so forth. A coiled basket of unknown provenience (possible Northern Paiute) in the author's collection has breaks in the continuity of stitching, which for short spans only surrounds the added foundation but does not link it to previous rounds, to produce four equally-spaced panels on the basket wall.

The stitching material may be colored for part of its application. Naively applied this will give colored bands around the basket. More elaborate application of colored stitching will produce geometric designs, human and animal figures, and the like.

Finally, the technique of imbrication (as Mason termed it) has had very limited use for ornamentation of coiled baskets. A decorative ribbon has a fold caught under the fiber of a sewing stitch. The ribbon-like strip is then folded in the direction of the work so as to cover the previous stitch before being caught under a new one. The imbricating strip is added to the basic foundation and stitching of the basket; it does not form a structural member of the ensemble. In theory the imbricating strip could be pulled from the surface of the basket without causing its collapse. Brittleness and rough handling have conspired to remove the strip from many baskets which once were imbricated, so that only the folded bit caught under each stitch remains. The technique of imbrication is a specialty of the Salishan-speaking Indians of the state of Washington and adjacent parts of British Columbia.

Woven Basketry

Following Mason's lead, it is possible to categorize woven basketry techniques as: checkerwork, diagonal or twilled, wickerwork, wrapped weft, or twined. Some observers of the basketry scene would separate twined work from this group and place it as a third major category, coordinate with coiled and woven basketry.

Checkerwork. Checkerwork usually involves the use of contrasting materials in each direction which are woven in a simple over-under (plain) weave. The fairly wide crossing elements are about the same width. As each element is alternately concealed or apparent as it crosses a series of other elements, a checkerboard pattern is produced (Figure 28). While this technique may be used for baskets, especially those of a rectangular shape, it is most commonly employed in the weaving of mats. These flat mats, hardly containers in the conventional sense, are marginal basketry, but the techniques used to weave them are inextricable from those used to produce basketry containers.

Figure 28

Checkerwork basketry

Diagonal or Twilled Basketry. Diagonal or twilled basketry can be divided into two categories. The diagonal work is comparable to the checkerwork above, except that it is woven off the selvage edge at forty-five degrees instead of at a right angle. Because the material is folded, initially, over the edge-forming strip, it will not display the color or texture contrast characteristic of checkerwork (Figure 29).

Figure 29

Diagonally woven basketry

Figure 30

Twilled basketry

Twilled basketry (Figure 30) is woven with the active element passing over or under more than one static element at a time. In succeeding rows the pattern is altered so that a systematic staggering of the crossings occurs. The angle and direction of the resulting diagonal twill may be changed by differences in relative size of the crossing elements and by changing the number of static elements crossed at a time. The more elements skipped, the lower will be the angle of apparent twilling. The sequence can be reversed at intervals to produce herringbone and diamond patterns. The twilling technique may be used with other than straight weaving, such as with twining (see below), to produce the diagonal effect.

Wickerwork. Wickerwork, which can be equated with basketwork in general, is here used in a restricted sense. Its basic technique is that of over-under weaving, but the elements are relatively large and the vertical ones quite stiff. The result is a "fabric" on which a series of vertical ridges appear prominently where the horizontal elements cross the verticals. The latter may be substantially concealed (see Figure 31).

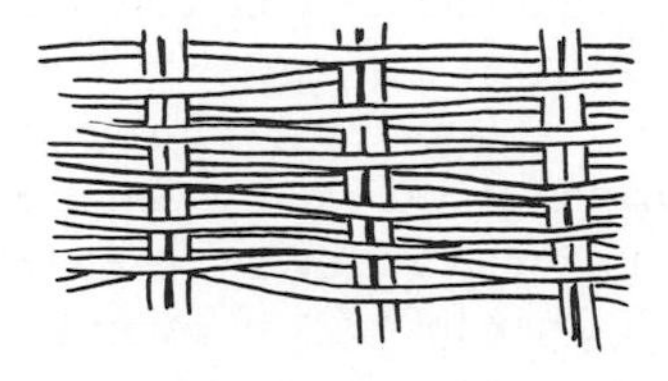

Figure 31

Wickerwork basketry

Wrapped Weft. In wrapped weft work the active element ("weft") makes one or more turns around the passive elements ("warps") which it crosses. These fastenings do not have to be on every vertical but may skip in a regular pattern to produce a twill or other ornamental effect. The active element may be simply turned about the vertical or it may be knotted at the crossing. The knotting would stabilize a basket in which the rows of active elements were widely spaced (Figure 32).

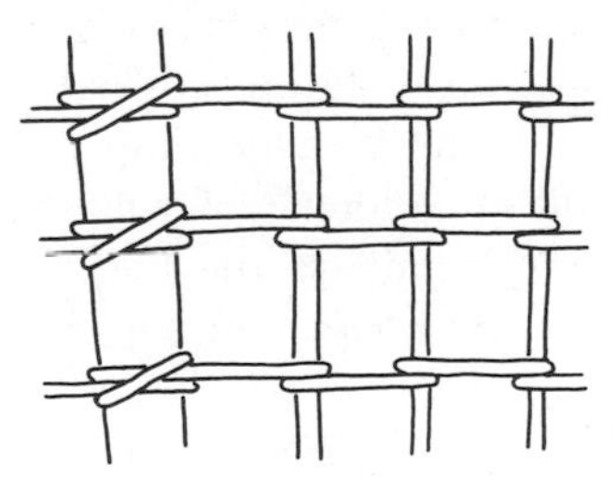

Figure 32

Wrapped weft basketry

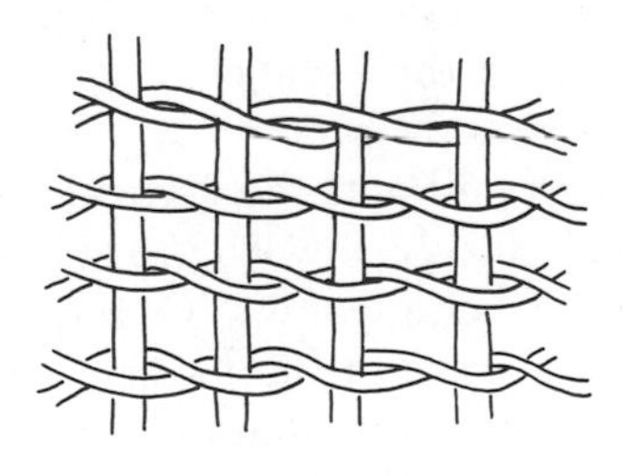

Figure 33

Twining of basketry

Twined Basketry. Twined basketry (Figure 33), often considered a separate major type in itself, is characterized by the twisting of the active elements about their longitudinal axis as they are worked across the passive elements (verticals, warps, standards). This means that the active elements are passed in pairs or triads or more. (A single weft can't be twisted in this fashion about its single axis.) If a pair of wefts are given a half-twist between adjacent warps, then each will appear alternately on one surface of the basket and then the other. If the paired wefts are given a full-twist between adjacent warps, then each weft will remain substantially on only one surface of the basket. In this latter case slightly more space is taken by the twisting so that there is a greater lateral spacing between adjacent warps. It is possible to capitalize on the space-using attribute of the twists by making several between warps in order to hold the warps apart, as in making a basketry sieve.

Techniques may be combined to produce a twilled twine. The scheme of crossings is progressively staggered to create a diagonal pattern of the wefts. This pattern is essentially the same as a woven twill except for the twisting of the wefts. Similarly, it is possible to incorporate a braiding technique: the several wefts passing across the warps are braided about each other instead of being twisted consistently in one direction.

The manners of starting a woven basket are more numerous than those of coiled basketry. It is possible to begin with a simple crossing of two pairs of strands of which the prolongations become verticals in the basket sides. Other strands may be added to the starting group, either laid across the others or woven with them. The starting strands may be tied together in any of several ways.

As the basket develops under the hand of the weaver, it becomes necessary to add vertical strands in order that the original strand spacing remain substantially the same with increasing circumference. These vertical strands are started by having the beginning end caught by a passage of the horizontal element(s).

The variety of ways of beginning a woven basket is substantially exceeded by the number of ways in which the edge may be finished. The simplest and crudest edge has no finish at all; the weaver simply stops weaving and cuts the vertical standards to the same length. Or an exceptionally heavy row (or rows) of twining may terminate the basket, the verticals being cut off. Or the verticals may be bent over and woven back into the body of the basket. Or they can be bent at ninety degrees and bound down by an applied whipping stitch. A separate rim element can be stitched to the raw upper edge of the basket. The verticals may be turned downward over a thin rim piece. There remain many other possibilities as well.

Appearance and Work Patterns

Beyond the few comments already made about the direction of coiling in coiled baskets there are related matters to consider when discussing basket weaving. Some of these are closely linked to the appearance of the basket.

All baskets have one side or surface which is more apparent than the other. It is to this "good" side, which is worked with care, that most of the ornament will be applied. The difference between good and poor sides of a basket is related to its shape and to the use to which it is put. In a flat basket or one with low, flaring sides, the inside (concave side) is likely to be the good side and to be decorated. In a basket with a constricted opening, either a shouldered form with a neck or a globular form, the ornamented and good side will be the exterior. A large open-mouthed basket presents problems, but suggests a consideration which may apply in other cases too: this basket may be decorated inside and out, with both sides quite visible unless the basket is customarily on view when filled, in which case the ornament is more likely to be outside. This may save the design from being obscured by accumulated stains from the basket contents.

The good side of a basket will display the greater care in placement of sewing stitches (coiling). Blemishes in materials, knots, loose ends, obvious overlaps of material — all will be on the poor side when possible. The splitting of stitches will be most regular on the good side, even though splitting may occur at both sides. In general, the good side reflects the attention given to its appearance and the poor side, the lack of care.

Aboriginal basket weavers when at work usually sit, squat, or kneel on the ground with their work resting on the ground or in the lap. This posture, the size of a basket, the location of the good side, and the direction in which the work progresses form a functional cluster. If, for example, the weaver works from left to right and the basket is to be ornamented on the concave side because it is relatively open, then the work will be conducted on the far edge of the basket (looking from the viewpoint of the weaver) if it can comfortably be reached. With the same direction of work but the outside of the basket "good," the weaver will probably work on the near edge of the basket.

A woven basket possesses work direction, just as a coiled basket does. The crossing of passive strands by an active strand occurs in a regular progression. The directional character is less pronounced in a simple woven basket than in certain kinds of twining in which the twined pair is carried around and around the basket as it grows upward, resulting in a style similar to the progression of coiled basketry.

Thus, a full description of basket making will include three correlated factors: the direction in which work progresses (left to right or the reverse); whether the weaver works on the near side or the far side of the basket; and the direction of coiling, if any. In the case of basketry materials derived archeologically, only the direction of coiling is evident. It may be possible to deduce the others when one knows the size of the basket and which is the good surface.

Materials

The materials used in basketry are as varied as are the several weaves, twines, and coiling techniques. Almost every part of plant materials, excepting possibly the fruits, are used by one group or another. The roots of shrubs and trees are prized because they are tough and flexible as well as strong. Gathering roots is, of course, destructive to the plant. (Only the gathering of leaves seems to affect the plant very little.) Once pulled up, the roots may be shaved to bring them to uniform diameters.

The stalks of shrubs, such as those of willows, may be used with only preliminary scraping or may be split into several elements. In the splitting of light basketry materials, industrial use is sometimes made of the teeth. The end of the element is first split into three with a knife, then one resulting end is held between the teeth and one end in each hand. The hands are then thrust away from the face and apart to separate the element into three strands. When the hands reach the extremes of extension, a fresh "bite" (literally!) is taken on the material, and the process is repeated.

The wood of a plant may have basketry uses. Splints can be split from wood, either with a cutting edge or by tearing. Torn splints have the advantage in strength of not violating grain lines but the disadvantage of rough appearance and variations in thickness. The outer bark of trees is rarely of much use in basketry, but the inner bark is prized. This fibrous material, stripped from the inside of bark slabs cut or peeled from trees, can be torn to uniform width and thickness. Cedar bark is a favorite for matting on the Pacific Northwest Coast of North America. Grasses are used in bundles and singly in basket making. And baleen (whalebone) is used by some Arctic peoples in their finer baskets. This roster does not, of course, exhaust the total list of materials used by aboriginal peoples in the making of baskets.

After being collected, scraped, split, and otherwise prepared for use, most basketry materials are soaked in water before use. This makes them flexible so that they can be bent, manipulated, and even tied without breaking. When they are dry again, they tend to retain the shape into which they have been forced. The knots tighten up, the tucked ends stay in place, and it is hard to realize that this stiff, bristly thing was recently soft and pliable. Not all basketry is stiff on drying; if the materials from which it is made are soft, then the end product will be soft too.

Social Aspects

Basketry among nonliterates is primarily a domestic craft practiced by women. It is ideally suited to this usage because an unfinished basket may be set aside indefinitely, yet work resumed on fifteen minutes' notice (the time to moisten basket and weaving strands). Although the materials and the product are light and potentially portable there is no evidence that work was conducted away from the dwelling area.

Men had little to do with basketry, even with the gathering and processing of materials. Only when basketry rose to a quasi-industrial level, as it infrequently did, were they involved. Men, for example, made the basketry boats (*gufa*) of Mesopotamia. On the modern scene men are the weavers of Dutch dike mats.

Because students of basketry have concerned themselves primarily with technical aspects of the craft we know very little more. A notable exception to this is the work of Lila O'Neale (1932) who investigated training and professionalism in addition to traditional concerns. Despite the general lack of information one is left with the impression that basketry was rarely professionalized or pursued industrially.

11

Weaving

Weaving is a process which involves the use of a loom. Some authorities consider that a true loom must have heddles to separate groups of warp yarns between which the wefts pass. Therefore, the practice of weaving can really be considered to be defined by the presence of heddling devices. Yet there are textiles, other than baskets, produced by "finger weaving" without the use of heddles. Despite difficulties in definition, there are, as in basketry, few problems recognizing the weaving process or its products at a common sense level.

An important feature which distinguishes the weaving of cloth from the weaving of basketry is the length of the strands used. In basketry the strands are of finite length, so that one is continually conscious of the end and of the necessity to add additional lengths. In weaving the yarns or strands are of effectively infinite length so that the need to add lengths is not so pressing. The strands of basketry are limited in length by their sources — roots, bark strips, leaf fibers, and so forth. The yarns of weaving can be spun to any length, limited only by one's patience and the capacities of one's yarn-handling equipment — bobbins, reels, warping drums, loom beams.

The Thread

Textile fibers found among preindustrial peoples included virtually all those known to us today with the exception of the synthetics — nylon, rayon, and the like. However, all fibers were not known to all peoples. Europeans used wool and flax. Ancient Egyptians and Indians had cotton, as did the prehistoric Indians of the American Southwest. Silk was confined to the Far East until recently. Elsewhere in the world a wide variety of fibers were spun and woven, from *Apocynum* in North America to New Zealand flax (*Phormium tenax*).

Animal hair and wool were derived from virtually all domesticates — sheep, goat, camel, horse, cow, llama, alpaca, yak, and dog. Indians of the Pacific Northwest raised a woolly variety of dog in order to have the wool for weaving; they had no other domesticated animal. These same people also secured a scanty supply of mountain goat wool by plucking it from the bushes where the goats had rubbed in passing or from the hides of occasional game animals.

Wools have to be freed from alien matter — twigs, dirt, manure — and aligned before they can be spun. The cleaning and aligning of wools is usually done with combs, teazles (a thistle head), and wool cards. The combs are not markedly different from those used in hairdressing. The cards consist of boards equipped with short handles from which a forest of little spines protrudes. They resemble the currying brushes used on horses today. Used in pairs, these cards are raked across each other so that the wool between is drawn out and the fibers straightened into parallel lines. After being brushed and rebrushed in this manner, the wool is rolled laterally off the card to form a loose roll which is set aside to be spun.

Cotton must be freed of its seeds as well as aligned before spinning. Combing and hand picking were both done but were not very efficient in their use of labor. A primitive gin, consisting of two rollers between which the cotton was forced, was used in India.

Bowing was a technique applied to wool and to cotton to separate tangled fibers. A heavy wooden bow, equipped with a string and sometimes devices to intensify its vibrations, was suspended from an overhead support. The operator steadied the bow so that its string just swept the surface of the fibers. When the string was vibrated by being struck with a club, it plucked at the tangled mass and loosened individual fibers (see Figure 34).

The preparation of flax is more complicated than that of some other vegetable fibers. The general outline of flax processing, however, is applicable to other plants possessing long fibers embedded in a woody stalk.

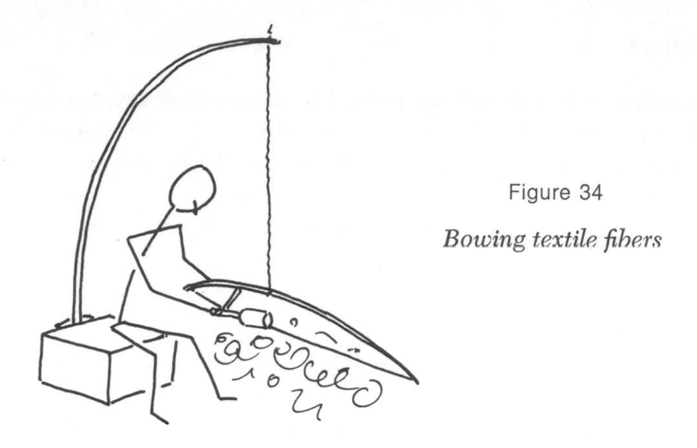

Figure 34

Bowing textile fibers

When flax is harvested, it may be pulled instead of being cut, because the latter approach loses some of the available length of fiber. After the seeds are stripped off, the fibers are loosened by retting (soaking) the flax stalks in a vat or pond, or by exposing them to moisture from dew or snow. When the bark loosens, the stalks are removed and dried. The breaking of the stalks can be conducted with a brake or by beating with a special club (swingle, scutch). Finally, the stalks are combed by drawing them through a fixed comb (hackle) set in a bench. Though some of these steps may be repeated in order to clean the fibers more thoroughly, retting, scutching, and combing leave the flax fibers in final shape for spinning.

Spinning

Once cleaned and aligned, the textile fibers must be spun into yarns. There are three steps in the spinning process: (1) drawing out combed fibers from the bundle of lightly twisted wool, cotton, or other material (the roving); (2) twisting these fibers about their long axis and about each other; and (3) winding the resulting thread on a spool or other holder. Primitive spinning devices and techniques may do one or two of these steps at once but not all three. Usually the winding, or taking up, constitutes a separate step.

Spinning can be done on the thigh without any equipment. Many peoples, wearing little more than a pubic apron or other abbreviated loin covering, find spinning with the hand rolling on the thigh convenient and employ it exclusively, though the results are rather uneven in drawing and twisting. Further, the technique is limited to short pieces of thread or cord because of the problem of snarling of the free, finished, but unwound, product.

Almost any type of spindle is an improvement over thigh spinning. The basic spindle consists of a shaft, eight to twenty-four inches long, equipped with a flywheel (whorl) or a crosspiece to sustain its rotation. The spindle and its weight can vary with the material being spun and the fineness of thread desired. In use the spindle is rarely kept in the hand, but instead is given a quick twist and released to continue its rotation. A simpler spindle is the "rested" type. This spindle, with its lower end in a cup on the ground, may be rolled on the thigh or twisted between the fingers to start its rotation. It was used by Indians of the American Southwest, as well as elsewhere in the world. It provides a better twist than the hand-on-thigh technique but does not draw out the thread very well. Better in this latter regard is the suspended (or drop) spindle which is spun between the fingers and dropped at the side of the spinner to continue its rotation. The weight of the spindle draws out the fibers of the developing thread quite uniformly (Figure 35).

Figure 35

Rested spindle

An adjunct to the spindle is the distaff on which is placed the roving from which fibers for the thread are drawn. In practice, the spinner draws fibers from the clump on the distaff; these are attached to the spindle which is given a twist between the fingers and dropped. The spindle continues to rotate and the spinner continues to feed more fibers until the spindle either slows or strikes the ground. Then the spun thread is wound on the spindle, replaced in the hook at the upper end, and the process repeated. With the distaff supported — by belt, sash, or arm — the spinner using a suspended spindle need not remain in one spot. Thus, spinning could be carried on in this fashion while en route to market or while tending herd animals (Figure 36).

Figure 36

Standing spinner with distaff

In the hands of an expert these primitive spindles could produce the finest, most even yarns. The Indians of Southern Asia and the prehistoric inhabitants of the Peruvian highlands were especially noted for their spinning abilities which have not been surpassed by any modern hand.

The hand spinning wheel (Figure 37) is the next, and a very recent, step in the development of spinning devices, probably originating in India in the first millenium A.D. and spreading from there. In scarcely altered form it was found in the early twentieth century from Iceland to

Figure 37

Hand spinning wheel

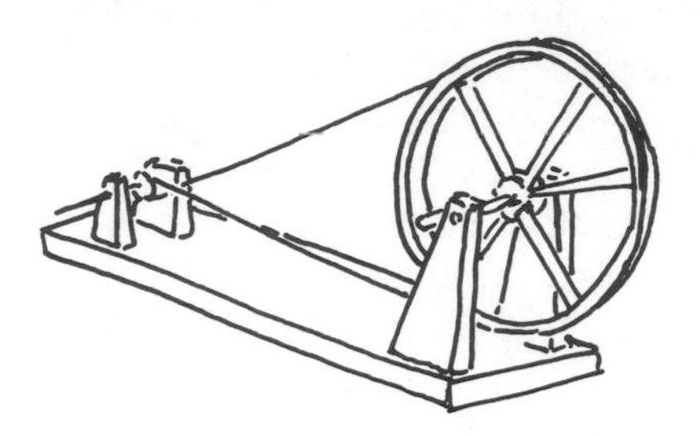

Japan. In addition, Europeans carried it to remote parts of the New World. This spinning wheel has a fixed spindle which is revolved by being belted with a cord to a large wheel turned by hand. As with several other spindles the supply of fibers (roving) is held on a distaff. A preliminary thread is hand spun and attached to the tip of the spindle. The wheel is revolved with one hand while the other draws out the fibers from the spindle. When the arm has reached its maximum extension the spinning is stopped. The hand is swung so that the yarn runs from the side of the spindle which is then turned in a reverse direction to wind on the spun yarn. Fresh roving is brought into the hand and the spinning resumed. When the spindle is full, the spun yarn is wound off onto a reel. It will be noted that even with partial mechanization of spinning, the winding step remained discrete from drawing and spinning.

Increasing population and affluence in Europe led to a rise in demands for textile products and, in turn, for yarns. The hand spinning wheel was an improvement over the old hand spindle but still was not adequate to the expanded task. By the late fifteenth century the flyer spindle had been developed. Its precise date and evolution are unknown because its earlier manifestations were kept secret by its users. Suffice it to say that this invention made a considerable impact by introducing a basic principle which is still fundamental to modern spinning machines.

The spinning wheel with a flyer spindle consists of a large wheel, originally turned by hand but later by a foot pedal connecting through cranks, belted to a spinning head. The head has the spindle shaft, the attached flyer, a spool or bobbin, and two driven pulleys. The spindle is hollow at one end with a lateral hole inside the arms of the flyer. The arms are equipped with a series of small hooks (or hecks). Concentric with the spindle is the bobbin shaft. The spindle shaft and the bobbin shaft each have separate pulleys, side by side, of different diameters. If the head has a smaller bobbin pulley, it is said to have a "bobbin lead," and if the reverse is true, it has a "flyer lead."

The whole assembly is turned by drive cords belting the pulleys to the large drive wheel, which is turned by hand or by a pedal-and-crank mechanism. Both spindle and bobbin turn in the same direction.

The thread being spun passes from the roving on the distaff, through the spinner's hand, through the passage in the spindle, over a hook on the flyer, to the bobbin. With a bobbin lead, the bobbin turns faster than the spindle-flyer combination, drawing the thread over a flyer hook and through the spindle shaft. (With a flyer lead, the flyer turns faster than the bobbin and, overtaking the latter, wraps the thread around it. This pulls thread over the hook and through the spindle shaft). Meanwhile the rotation of the assembly twists the thread, and the "draw" is controlled by the spinner's hand.

As spinning proceeds the thread must be moved from heck to heck to approximate level winding on the bobbin. The filling of the bobbin increases its diameter and the speed of thread drawing. The spinner must hold back on the thread to keep it from being inadequately twisted before being drawn onto the bobbin; the drive cord slips on the bobbin pulley by way of compensation. Cord tension is, therefore, important for satisfactory operation. Two independent driving cords may be used, but tensioning is easier if the driving cord is a single one making two loops. On some spinning wheels the drive cords form a figure eight to reverse rotation of the spindle head. From time to time the spinner must stop forward progress to wind the thread off the bobbin. It is taken off onto a separate reel.

The direction of the twist of yarns is significant just as other nominally arbitrary details may be. Customarily the direction of twist is described as either "S-twist" or "Z-twist" (respectively, sinistral or dextral) in recognition of the slope of the central element in these letters. It will be found that spinners can produce yarns in one twist or the other, the choice depending upon the uses to which the yarns will be put. Some of these choices reflect tradition, and others have a functional basis. It is reported that some weavers prefer to have warp yarns of one twist and weft yarns of the other. The function, if any, of this practice is obscure. However, when spun yarns are twisted together to form a multi-plied string, then it is functional that the twist of the spinning be opposite to that which forms the string. So, one finds strings which are S-spun and Z-twist or vice versa.

Loom Types

The loom is essential, by definition, to the process of weaving. Though there are many variations, looms may be classified into two basic types: those with bars and those with beams. The capabilities and the manner of use depend on this distinction.

Both bars and beams are the transverse elements at the ends of a loom. They may form a part of its frame, or they may be inside the frame. A loom may have functional substitutes in place of a true bar or beam. The bar is defined as the end element of a loom around which the warp passes. The warp yarns form either a simple open loop or a figure eight loop. They may be a single strand of yarn wound many times in this fashion. The beam is defined as the end element of the loom to which is fastened the end of the warp. (Commonly each end of a warp yarn is fastened to a beam but not the same beam.) In the case of a bar-type loom the length of the warp is strictly governed by the distance between the two bars. It is either that distance (less a small amount for technical reasons) or else twice that distance if a simple loop warp is used. In the case of a beam-type loom, the distance between beams has no direct bearing on the length of the warp. Warp in excess of the true distance between the beams is wound onto the beams, the only limits being those of setting up the warp and the capacity of the beams.

For the sake of clarity in the discussion it would be well to define warp and weft at this point, though we will not be concerned with them in detail. The term warp is applied to the yarns which are first placed on the loom. The strands run the long way of the woven cloth. In the weaving process the warp yarns are separated, in groups, so that the weft yarns may be inserted. The term weft refers to the yarns which are actively woven across the warp. Though the warp yarns necessarily run from end to end of the fabric (or the loom), the individual weft yarns need not run the full width of the fabric. However, weft yarns must, collectively, cross the span of the warp from edge to edge so that their "lacing" of the warps converts a bundle of parallel yarns into a fabric.

The simplest type of loom is a one-bar loom (Figure 38) in which the warps do not form continuous loops, either open or figure eight, but are a series of discrete yarns, each hung over the bar. The one-bar loom, sometimes called a suspended warp loom, was used natively on the Pacific Northwest coast. This kind of loom frequently lacks a proper set of heddles (which makes it a dubious loom in the first instance) and is

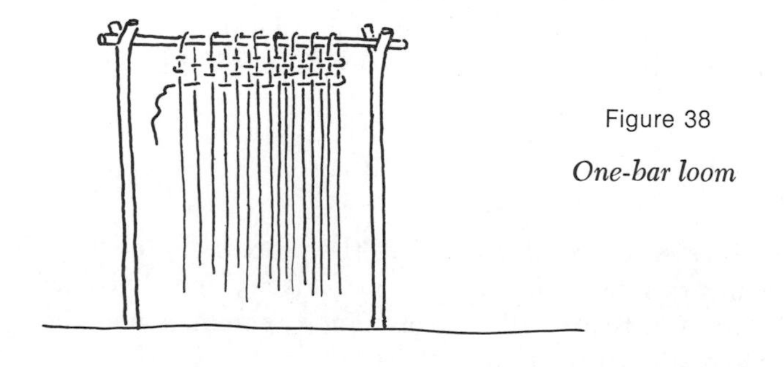

Figure 38

One-bar loom

associated with the finger weaving technique. The wefts are carried across by making the warp crossings one at a time instead of separating warps in groups with the aid of heddling devices. For obvious reasons the one-bar loom places the warps in a vertical plane.

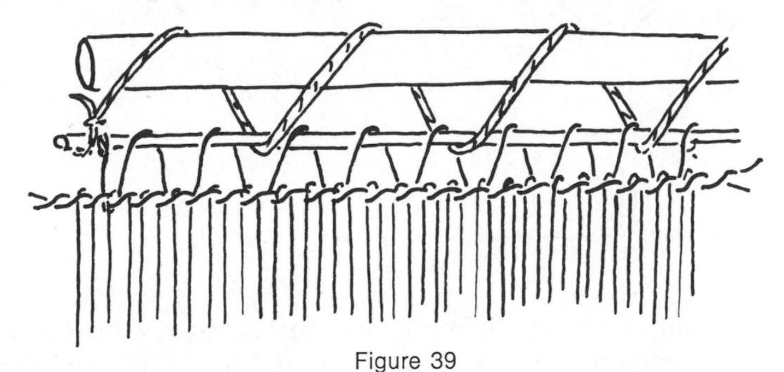

Figure 39

Detail of end selvage cord

The two-bar loom is a more common form which is more conventional with regard to accessory parts and their operations. In either horizontal or vertical planes the heddling devices may be elaborated to provide full control. On elaborated forms of this loom, as in parts of the American Southwest, the bars are replaced by cords about which the warp yarns turn — a substitution which alleviates many problems when beginning and ending the fabric. Unlike a wooden bar, the cord can remain in the end selvage of the cloth and is easier to remove, if that is desired, without leaving a looseness of warps at that point (Figure 39). Because the unsupported cord would bow inward under the pull of the warp yarns, it is lashed to a rigid support. These lashings may also play a role in the maintenance of proper warp tension. As the weaving proceeds, the warps are more or less crimped and shortened. At some point in the system there must be a way of reducing the rising tension on the warp.

A variant form of the two-bar loom is the frameless two-bar loom, also called a belt loom or a back-strap loom (Figure 40). The two bars are not held apart by the side pieces of a frame. Instead one bar is fastened to a fixed object such as a tree, a house post or beam, or a stake in the ground. The other bar is attached to a harness which passes behind the back (or upper waist) of the weaver. Tension is controlled by the weight which the weaver, usually sitting on the ground, throws back against this strap. The working area of such a loom must be close to the weaver, within comfortable arm's reach. Therefore, the style of warping is the open loop rather than a figure eight because the former may be shifted around as weaving progresses to keep the working area at hand. Looms of this type are best adapted to handling narrower fabrics. When wider

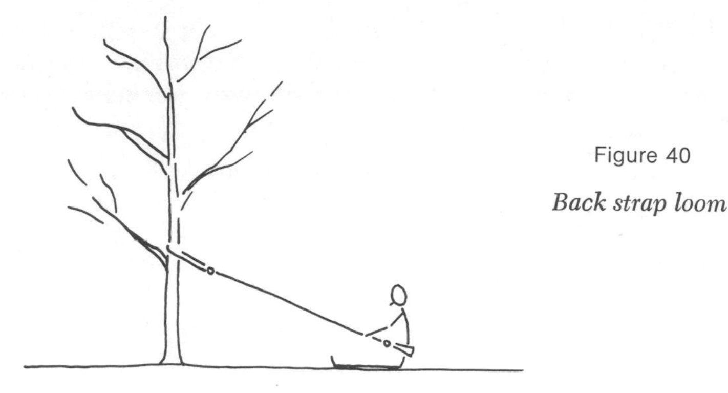

Figure 40

Back strap loom

cloths are desired, they may be woven in strips on such a loom and then sewn together, edge to edge. Both stability of loom and convenience of reach put a limit of about two feet on the width of fabrics woven on a frameless loom. The major advantage of this loom is its small size when not in use (rolled up) and thus its portability.

Like the version with a bar, the one-beam loom may be called a suspended warp loom. Therefore, one must not accept uncritically the use of this term. In the one-beam loom, again with a vertical orientation, the lengths of warps are fastened individually to the beam. As cloth is woven it is wound into the beam. The excess lengths of warp yarns, if any, are gathered up in pendant hanks or else neatly coiled into bags hanging, by these yarns, below the working area of the loom. The gathered warps may be weighted to control warp tension; if this is so, then the loom may be called a weighted warp loom. Neither the term "weighted warp" nor the term "suspended warp" falls in line with our basic typology because either of them might refer to a loom with a bar or one with a beam. The one-beam loom is more likely to have heddles than a one-bar loom. It can be used to weave considerable lengths of cloth and so profits substantially from this elaboration (See Figure 41).

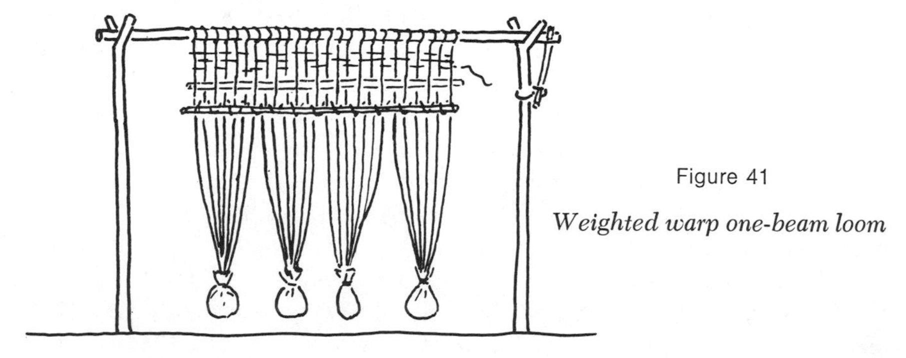

Figure 41

Weighted warp one-beam loom

The two-beam loom is, typologically, the perfected form of hand loom. On one beam is wound, initially, the bulk of the warp yarns and on the other the cloth as weaving progresses. Various devices of pawls and ratchets, levers, and counterweights are used to keep a proper tension on the warp. Spanning the warp yarns are the heddles and, usually, a reed batten to pack down the wefts as they are inserted.

Two-beam looms are customarily fully framed but need not be so. The Chinese recently used a frameless two-beam loom whose warp "beam" consisted of a bucket in which the excess warp was flaked down. Its cloth "beam" consisted of a stick around which the woven ribbon was wound. The loom, using a card heddle (a very simple, single heddle), was set up over a table which formed an extemporaneous frame. The whole could be rolled up easily and tucked into the bucket for storage, making it in every way as portable and convenient as the more common frameless two-bar loom.

The fully framed two-beam loom, in styles traditional in both Europe and the Far East, often has its web passing over several transverse frame members instead of being organized in a straight line. In this way the beams can be placed where convenient and clear of the working area. The working area can be brought close to a seated weaver and the heddling controls become a bit sophisticated. The result is a compact, well-organized loom (Figure 42).

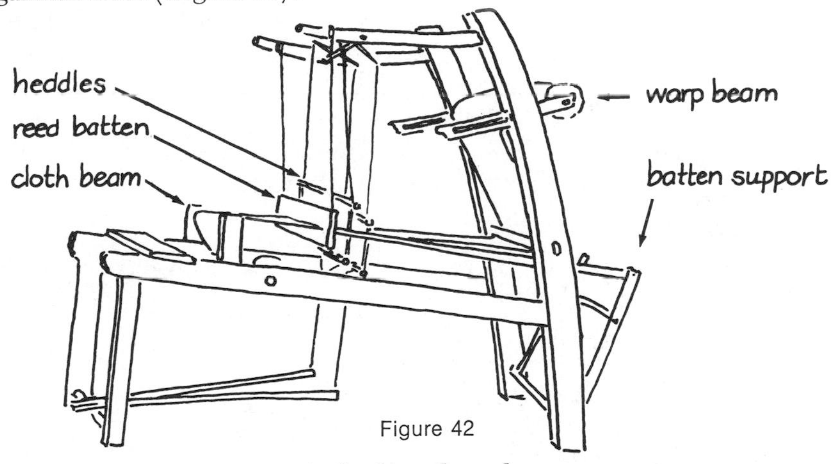

Figure 42

Evolved two-beam loom

As a bit of a curiosity, there is also the traveling loom. This may be based on either the two-bar or the two-beam concept. The essence of this loom is that the weaving station is movable and, as the work progresses, travels along the length of the warp. In this fashion the heddles and other elements are brought to the work rather than the other way around. The warp is usually stretched out between two anchors — trees, stakes, or sled-like structures. A variant, with a resemblance by way of the stretched out warp, has the warp fed through a fixed weaving station. The weaving station is sheltered, but the warp is strung out in the open air.

Warping of the loom is prerequisite to weaving. The placing of the warp yarns may be a simple or a complex operation, coordinate with the nature of the loom and the fabric which will be woven on it. A suspended warp loom may be warped simply by attaching each warp yarn in turn to the top beam or by looping each warp yarn over the top bar, depending on the type of loom. Considering the situation, warping will probably be done directly on the loom. For other looms it is customary to set up the warp yarns off the loom and then transfer them. This initial set-up makes use of warping stakes. Around these stakes, spaced to match the spacing of the loom bars, the warp yarn is wound in either an open loop or a figure eight pattern. The accumulated warp yarns, often held by transverse ties or sticks, are carefully shifted to the loom bars.

The placing of many warp strands for a long loom could involve much walking. The bars of a two-bar loom are rarely very far apart, perhaps ten or twelve feet for a back-strap loom. For a two-beam loom the amount of warp which may be required at first could be much more. If one were to use sixty feet of warp, with a fabric width of thirty inches, and a thread (warp) count of forty to the inch (not a very fine cloth), then placing the warp yarns over stakes would involve walking seventy-two thousand feet (13.63 miles). Far easier would be the use of a warping frame or board (Figure 43) which would place the whole stretch of the warp within arm's reach. A frame with twelve runs of five feet will reach the sixty-foot length.

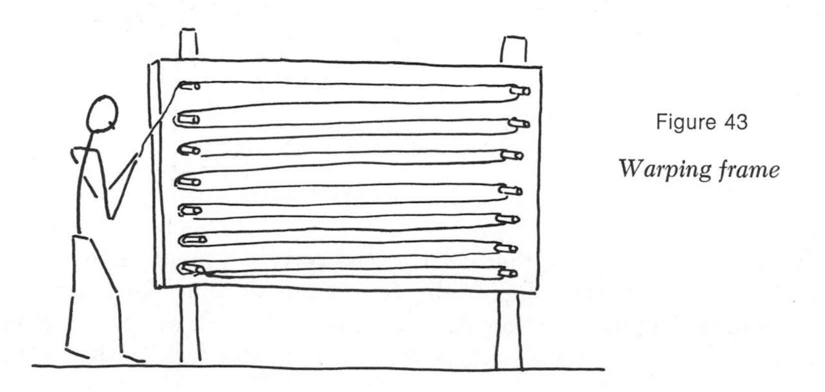

Figure 43

Warping frame

Because it is rarely possible to set up the entire warp on the stakes or frame, it is done in sections. Each section, when strung, may be picked up in a loosely-knotted hank using linked overhand knots to shorten and control the yarns. The hanks may be opened out and threaded directly on the loom. However, in a more elaborated technique, the hanks may be wound onto a reel before being placed on the loom. Reels, which certainly occupy a status inferior to those of looms and spinning wheels, are the unsung heroes of handling long yarns.

Heddles

The heddles may be involved in the process of stringing the loom. However, this may not be so with the simpler heddling devices, the simplest of which is the shed rod, a plain stick which passes under or behind every other warp string. When this rod is lifted or pulled, it moves these warps in relation to the other half of the warps. Some will not accord the shed rod the title of a heddle, but it does serve the same purpose.

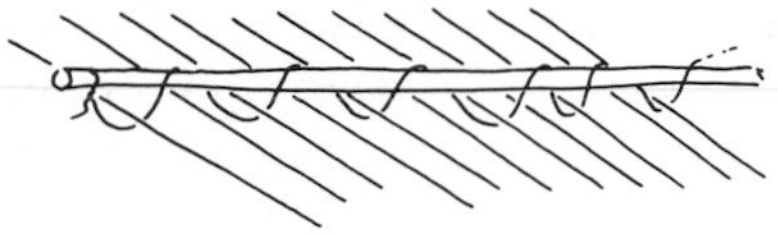

Figure 44

String heddle

The stick or string heddle (Figure 44), often used in conjunction with a shed rod, is widely employed by primitive weavers. It consists of a stick spanning the warp (sometimes only a substantial part) to which is tied a string forming loops which pass slackly around alternate warps. With the slack in the loops, the string heddle can retain its "grip" on one set of warps while the other set is raised by the shed rod. Because the same is not true of the shed rod, it must be slid away from the seat of operations when the string heddle is raised. In more complicated weaves by primitive weavers the number of string heddles is increased. This must be done to weave twilled fabrics. The number of shed rods cannot be increased for the same purpose but must remain at one.

Another simple heddle, which can be used alone (taking the place of both shed rod and string heddle), is the card heddle. Taking its name from its flat, or card-like, appearance, the card heddle consists of a plane of wood, or another rigid sheet material, with alternate slots and holes. One set of warps passes through the holes, the other through the slots. The card actually controls only one set of warps, those which pass through the holes, but it is capable of raising or depressing this set. To depress them is equivalent to raising the other set of warps, so the net effect is that of two heddles. The card need not be cut from a solid piece of material. In some cases the card heddle consists of a series of splines held in a frame, each spline having a hole, and a slot being left between adjacent splines. However, whatever its actual construction, the card has a limited capacity for warps. Consequently, card heddles find their greatest use on looms used to weave belts or ribbons, that is, very narrow fabrics. Even on these the warps must splay out from their normal spacing to pass through the array of holes and slots in the card (see Figure 45).

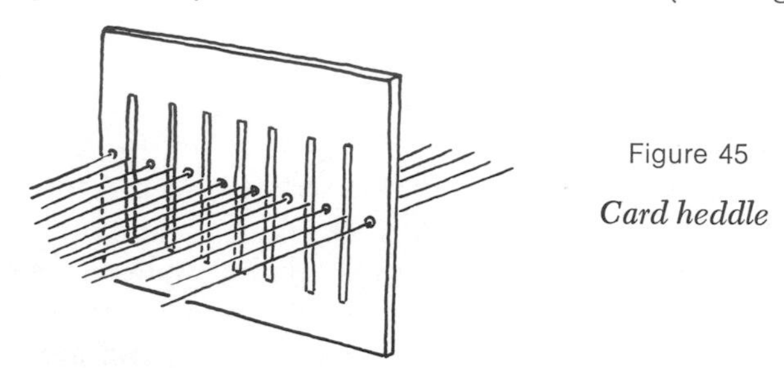

Figure 45

Card heddle

A further elaboration of heddles, still among preindustrial peoples though not necessarily nonliterate ones (as in European and Chinese peasant cultures), replaces the string heddle with a framed form (Figure 46). In this type the individual elements carrying warps are string loops spanning a frame. Each loop carries a warp yarn belonging to the set which the heddle controls. The frame itself is raised or depressed, bringing with it the loops and their warps. A modern version of this heddle, which is used in handcraft weaving, has wire or stamped metal loops replacing the string ones.

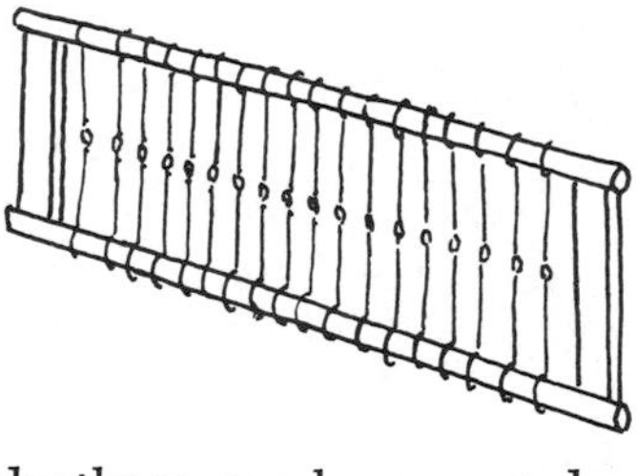

Figure 46

Framed string-loop heddle

The heddles can be handled independently or can be arranged so that their movements are coordinated. The shed rod and string heddles usually have no auxiliaries to control them; they are moved directly by hand. On some horizontal looms there exist props, like forked supports stuck into the ground, which will hold the rod or heddle stick in a raised position. Generally, though, these simple heddles do not have any associated harness. The framed heddle on an elaborated loom lends itself very well to coordination with its mates. Each heddle frame is connected, more or less directly, to a pedal with which the weaver can pull it down. Above, each frame is connected over a rocking arm or a pulley to the upper side of another heddle. Thus, when one heddle is pulled down by the pedal, its linked mate is pulled up by the connecting cords. In this fashion the required movement of the heddles can be reduced because each set (nominal half) of warps is moved only half the distance needed to open a shed. The general name for these links is harness.

The arrangement described above is used when only two heddles are involved. More elaborate weaves make additional heddles necessary. These may be linked in groups so that a pedal movement controls more than two heddles. When changes in the heddling pattern are necessitated by changes in the weave, they can be accomplished by rerigging the harness instead of simply altering the order in which the pedals are pressed.

Because the warp yarns pass through most heddles, it should be evident that attention must be paid to them when warping a loom. If a two-bar loom is warped using a figure eight pattern, then the warp yarns are automatically segregated into two groups. If the alternate warps are all that are needed for the projected weaving then they are readily picked up. The shed rod is passed through one of the openings already present, and the string heddle loops are passed down through one warp set to encircle the yarns of the other set. Both of these acts can be done after the warps are on the loom.

If a card heddle is to be used, then the warps must be drawn through it as they are being put on the loom. The heddle is a part of the original setup. This makes it doubly difficult to change one's mind about the pattern of weaving after the initial decision has been made. The string heddle, by contrast, can be removed and replaced with another pattern for heddling.

When the framed loop heddle of recent times is used, it, like the card heddle, is usually strung along with the rest of the loom. As the yarns are taken from the reel they are drawn through the several heddles before being attached to the warp beam. Sometimes to reduce the labor of reequipping a loom with warp, the ends of the old warp are left through the heddles and the new lengths tied on. After this the new warp is drawn through the heddles. The special knots used, usually termed weavers' knots, will pass through the loops of the heddles, for they have a minimum of bulk.

Battens and Shuttles

The reed batten (Figure 47), if used, is one other element in the system which must be in place as the warps are strung. Found among more sophisticated peasant weavers, this batten resembles the framed heddle of the same peoples. A rectangular frame spans the warps. Across the frame are a series of thin splines between which pass the warp yarns

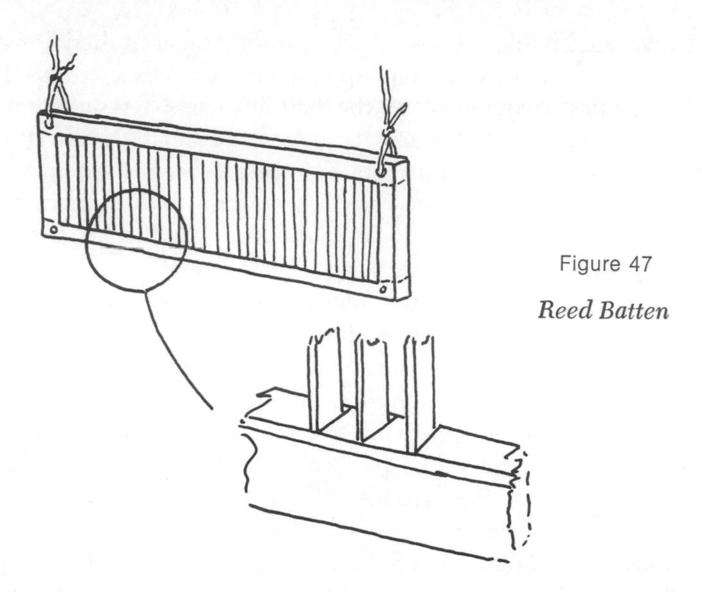

Figure 47

Reed Batten

which are free to move in the slots. As the heddles are worked, the yarns can move up or down without hindrance. There are not necessarily as many splines or slots as there are warp yarns; it is not as in the framed heddle where strict account must be taken of the position of every strand. Consequently, two or more strands may pass through a single slot. After a weft yarn has been drawn between the separated warps, it is packed ("battened") into place by moving the batten against it. The effect is that of a comb being drawn through the warps, but the action is more that of a blow struck by the batten. This type of batten is commonly suspended on cords or arms from the overhead portion of the loom frame. The weaver only has to pull it to strike against the accumulating weft.

Having gathered, carded, and spun the yarn and strung a loom with it, the weaver is ready to proceed. The weft yarns traverse the warps and hold them together laterally. The resulting fabric, then, has strengths in both directions. The procedure in a plain weave is to move the heddling devices so as to open a space (a "shed") between sets of opposing warps. The weft is passed through, one such passage being spoken of as a "pick" of weft. The batten, of whatever style, is used to pack down the weft. The heddles are reversed to open the opposing shed, and the process is repeated.

When weaving on a developed loom in which the heddles are foot-controlled, there is little problem in holding open a shed. On a loom using string heddles or a shed rod it is difficult to hold the heddle while passing the weft through the shed. The sword batten (see Figure 48), a stick with a flattened oval cross section, is inserted in the shed and turned

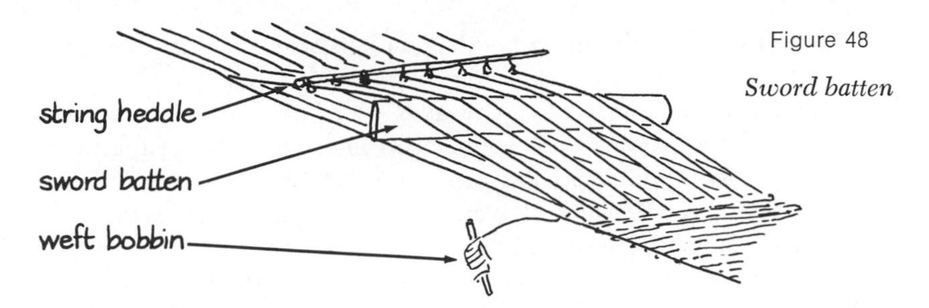

Figure 48
Sword batten

on edge so as to hold the warp sets apart. After the pick of the weft the batten is turned into the plane of the warps and thrust against the weft to pack it down. The batten must then be removed before the heddles can be reversed. This kind of batten is most commonly used by primitive weavers.

The weft cannot easily be passed as a loose hank through the opening of the shed. Usually it is wound on a bobbin of some sort — a little reel, a stick, or something similar. A proper shuttle may be used and is common for plain weaves among more sophisticated weavers. (For very short picks of weft, as in some tapestries, a shuttle would be a nuisance.) The shuttle has a smooth contoured shape — elliptical or boat-like — which makes it easy to pass through a shed. It may be elongated and weighted at the ends so that it can be slid rapidly through the shed, resting on the taut lower warps. In a depression or cavity of the shuttle is a bobbin with the weft yarn on it. These bobbins can be replaced as exhausted or as a color change is in order. In very fancy work the weft yarn emerges from a hole at the end of the shuttle. In other cases, it unreels directly from the bobbin cavity.

There are many specialized auxiliaries which may be employed by weavers, such as hooks for fishing through warp yarns or supports for the heddles of a horizontal loom. Among these auxiliaries are the tenters or their homologues. These are sticks with notched or sharpened ends which span the warps close to the working area to keep the tension of the weft from drawing in the sides of the fabric. In place of the sticks which operate in compression, one may find hooks fastened to the loom frame operating in tension.

Some Weaves

The complexity of possible weaves bears a low correlation to the complexity of the loom. In some respects there is almost a negative correlation in that the most complex weaves may result from finger weaving. Complexity of looms and subsidiary parts is most closely linked with ease and speed of the desired work. Generally speaking, the more complex the weave pattern desired, the more heddles will be used. Other than that, one cannot say much about the capabilities of a given loom.

A few of the commoner types of weaves will be reviewed here, with emphasis on their relation to the mechanism and operation of the loom.

The plain weave, which is basic to many textiles, is woven with a simple over-under relationship of weft to warp. Each weft passes over one warp and under the next. The next pick of weft alternates to pass under the ones which were previously passed over. If the warp and weft yarns are much the same and are equal in tension, neither will predominate on the surface of the cloth. Through differences in yarn size, tension, and battening, it is possible to make either warp or weft prevail on the surface. The results are known, respectively, as warp-face and weft-face. There are, additionally, a number of special trade names given to fabrics with these, and other, characteristics.

With only minor changes the plain weave approach can be varied to handle warps or wefts either singly or in pairs. Thus, one weft at a time may cross warps in pairs or two wefts at a time may make a single pick. When a pair of wefts are carried across paired warps the resulting fabric is called a basket weave. Alterations in the number of weft yarns can be made freely, while changes in warps, such as pairing, require changes in the stringing of the heddles.

In plain weaves and their variants, the major decorative effects come from differences in aspect (warp-face or weft-face), from differences in texture between warp and weft or between various parts of each, and differences in color of warp or weft portions. It is very easy to produce lateral bands of color, from edge to edge, by changing the weft color. Longitudinal stripes are also easily produced if the loom has been warped with some colored and some plain warps. Other color effects can be produced where stripe and band intersect.

Twilled weaves are accomplished by carrying wefts repeatedly over or under some warps in a regular pattern. The pattern of crossing is stepped laterally so as to produce a diagonal effect on the surface of the cloth. By reversing the direction of the diagonal at regular intervals, it is possible to create diamond, zigzag, and related patterns. The angle of the twill is controlled by the number of warps passed over at one time. For example, if the weft follows a scheme of over two and under one, the resulting apparent angle will be higher (closer to the longitudinal dimension of the cloth) than if the pattern is over four and under one.

In addition to ornamentation provided by the twilling of the weave, twilled fabrics can have effects created by changes in texture and color. These can be accomplished without alterations in the heddling setup. Reversals and similar forms result from changes in the order of use of the heddles not from their restringing, though changes in the nature of the twill do require changes in heddling.

Tapestry weaves are produced by carrying a given pick of weft less than the full width of the fabric. Other wefts will be passed through the same shed, but over different warp sections. Each weft, then, works back and forth in its own territory, creating a design element, a block of color, or texture.

The failure of a tapestry weft to go from edge to edge of the fabric creates some structural problems. The weft must turn back at some point. Its territory abuts that of another weft. If the two wefts, at their line of meeting, turn back around a common warp then the tapestry is called interlocking. If they turn back at adjacent warps, a noninterlocking tapestry (kelim, or slit tapestry) results. In each instance a problem arises. If the wefts turn about a common warp, this warp will come to have twice as many wefts packed on it as do the adjacent warps. This will in time create space problems and crowding; it cannot be tolerated for long distances. On the other hand, if the wefts turn about adjacent warps, a longitudinal slit (kelim) will form which will weaken the lateral strength of the fabric if it continues very long.

Though the tapestry offers much to the weaver desiring to produce a patterned cloth, it also has some limitations. The problems of the lateral edges of weft areas can be met by keeping these lines quite short; a brief slit can be tolerated. The borders can be kept straight, on the average, but stepped back and forth in small increments. This can be done with either interlocking or noninterlocking borders; the important point is that the critical area be diffused. Or, a long slit generated in weaving may be closed later by hand sewing.

Related to the concept of pattern formation by tapestry weaving is the practice of weft "floating." A float is a yarn which travels some distance on the surface (usually the back side) of the fabric between points where it is woven with the other yarns. It is more common for wefts to be floated than for warps. Usually the float occurs where a short run of apparent weft is desired, then a weft of another color, then another short run of the original weft, and so forth. Instead of having each bit of weft separate, one long yarn is used but carried along out of sight much of the time. The intervening stretches of weft can be built up in true tapestry style as discrete blocks of weaving. Floated fabrics, of course, do not appear the same on both surfaces. Furthermore, the float yarns are subject to snagging. So the emphasis is usually on ornament rather than utility.

Weaving is, in summary, a complex of coordinated activities which require skill, foresight, and patience. Though simple equipment can be found, the products of nonliterate weavers rival those of more sophisticated peoples. It will be noted that the simplest of weaving methods, finger weaving, can do anything which more complex equipment can do and much more because it is infinitely flexible. The major contributions of modernization in spinning and weaving are ease and speed; otherwise, there is little new under the sun in this area of technology.

12

Pottery

Pottery, or ceramic ware, is one of the first synthetic materials created by man. It owes its existence to the irreversible change brought about when clays are heated to drive off the water of hydration. Only exceptionally does this change occur in nature; thus ceramics are not a feature of the natural world. The discovery of this potentiality of the material brought into being a substance which man has found useful ever since.

Pottery seems to have had multiple origins, with at least one origination in the Old World and one in the New World. The Old World origin is obscure, but the best estimate suggests that pottery developed following the first sedentary food production in the Near East, perhaps on the western fringes of the Iranian Plateau, about 6000 B.C. From here the idea spread in all directions: to the east across India, across central Asia to north China, into Egypt and from there south through Nubia and then to western Africa. Pottery moved into Europe through its southeastern quarter and along the northern Mediterranean shore.

It is generally supposed the New World pottery arose independently of that in the Old World. Migrants probably left northeastern Asia before pottery reached that area. Late migrants, such as the Eskimo, may have brought the technology with them but to a hemisphere where it was already established. There is considerable argument about the point of original invention in the Americas. Currently favored is northwestern South America — Ecuador and Colombia — where pottery has been dated about 3000 B.C. To the north and south of this area the earliest pottery occurs as much as one thousand years later.

In some parts of the world pottery played only a minor part, if any. SubSaharan Africa placed less emphasis on pottery than on craft work in other media; anthropologists and other observers have echoed this lack of concern in producing a record, in archeology and ethnography, which is thin but seems to reflect accurately the secondary nature of this craft. The native Australians had no pottery unless some, unknown to the author, found its way into extreme northern Australia. If so, this would certainly be a reflection of its use in either Indonesia or the Melanesian area. The western Pacific islanders had some pottery, as in Micronesia and Melanesia; islands of the central and eastern Pacific area did not continue to use pottery after migration to these areas from the west. Coral islands, without clays, and recent volcanic islands, with limited clay deposits, did not offer much in raw materials. Additionally, these areas had good containers of coconut shells, large seashells, and leaves. When these natural vessels were available with little labor and the making and firing of pottery involved substantial outlays of work, then the choice was clear. It is possible also that a fuel shortage on some islands may have inhibited pottery making even when other materials were at hand.

Some early cultural evolutionists postulated a connection between the making of pottery and the Neolithic stage of man's existence. At one time pottery and ground stone tools were two of the main leitmotivs of this Age, but the emphasis today in defining the Neolithic is upon the production of food through plant cultivation and animal husbandry. There is still a trace of the earlier view in the recognition by some prehistorians of a Pre-pottery Neolithic phase in the Near East, but this is somehow not considered to be the true Neolithic.

Pottery was made by a number of people who were not food producers but subsisted by hunting, gathering, and related methods. Among such people were the Alaskan Eskimo and some of the California Indians. However, neither of these instances can be called independent. The Eskimos probably acquired their skill somewhere in northeastern Siberia, close at hand, while the Californians were in contact with pottery-making Indians in the American Southwest.

None of the foregoing, though, should be permitted to obscure the general circumstance — most pottery in the hands of primitives or nonliterates was made by sedentary peoples whose mode of life is closely linked to a Neolithic subsistence economy. Such a way of life also encouraged the making of containers which, however useful, were fragile and heavy. At another level, the sedentary life made feasible the making of kilns associated with advanced pottery making. And, even more remotely, this sedentary life may have encouraged the production of storage containers (which many pots are) by creating a surplus of storable food and goods.

The nature of clays is such that they can be dried and wetted time and again without undergoing any permanent change. The moisture involved in this process is called the water of plasticity. When clay is heated to a temperature in excess of approximately five hundred degrees centigrade, then another kind of water, the water of hydration, is driven off. The molecules of the water of hydration are chemically bonded to the compounds which form the clays; once they have been removed, they cannot be replaced. The clay is not simply dehydrated but has become another material — pottery or ceramic — which does not contain any water of plasticity to be added or subtracted at will. It is substantially unchanged by the presence of moisture.

Pottery-making peoples have a supply of clay at hand which is dug out and carried to the work area. There the dried lumps are pulverized and sifted, or winnowed, to remove coarse bits. The resulting fine particles are utilized directly by some potters. If even finer clay is desired, the sifted clay can be washed. It is dissolved in a large quantity of water, causing coarse particles eventually to settle to the bottom while colloidal particles remain in suspension. When water is poured off and evaporated to recover the colloids, the clay is then said to be levigated.

Tempering

Some clays are ready to use for pottery as they come from the clay pits; the only preparation they need is grinding and the addition of proper amounts of water. Most clays are modified because it is believed that the addition of "temper" will reduce cracking in drying and firing. Tempering materials vary widely, and one gets the impression that almost anything added will produce the desired result. Organic materials — chopped straw, rice and rice hulls, manure, bone, various plant fibers — are recorded ethnographically and archeologically. Inorganic materials — quartz sand, mica, feldspar, ground-up fragments of old pottery ("grog"), shell, sponge spicules, limestone, and other stony items — are also noted. (Admittedly some of these "inorganic" materials, for example, shell, are ultimately organic. However, they are listed here because of their stony nature.) The organic tempering materials are usually burned out of the pottery during firing. Their sometime presence is evident through the cavities which are left. The choice of tempering material is, like other parts of the process of potting, culturally controlled. Consequently the temper has cultural, as well as technical, significance and is a favorite of archeologists seeking to distinguish one kind of pottery from another.

It is necessary to bring the clay to a homogeneous state with an even distribution of moisture and with the air pockets worked out. To accomplish this the clay is kneaded, cut, reformed, and pounded many times. Water can be added to the clay or removed by this working. The clay is usually allowed to age before use.

Shaping

Shaping by hand of the material of the pot body (the so-called paste) can be carried out by any one or more of several methods: excavating, modeling, coiling, paddling, and molding. Historically handmade pottery substantially antedates wheelmade pottery. The potter's wheel was developed in the Near East by 4000 B.C. and spread slowly from there to much of the Old World. However, it did not penetrate prehistorically to SubSaharan Africa. Despite the sophisticated pottery of the New World, especially in the Meso-American civilizations, the potter's wheel was unknown there until after the time of Columbus.

Excavating a lump of clay in order to form a bowl is a very simple method. It is used more often to start another method than employed as the sole shaping technique. Once a cavity is formed, it can be enlarged by paddling.

Hand modeling is a widespread method of shaping clay. With care the method can produce fine work and shapes which can be made in no other way. Like excavating, the modeling technique may precede some other method. Some tools — a scraper, a smoother, or a point — may be adjuncts to the thumbs and fingers in this technique. Finger or thumb marks may be left visible for ornamentation.

Coiling of pottery involves the forming of long cylinders of clay by rolling the material between the palms or, less frequently, between the hand and a plane surface. The resulting pieces are placed in a continuous coil (spiral, helix, or helical-spiral) to form the body of the vessel. Alternatively, the clay can be formed into concentric rings which are stacked to form the vessel. The joints in the rings and the joints between portions of the coil are usually staggered to avoid forming a line of weakness. The coils are pressed firmly together to weld them into a unit. Infrequently the individual coils are left to show as a design feature; more commonly the joints are smoothed over to make them virtually invisible.

When a coiled pot breaks it may do so along the lines of poorly made joints between coils.

Excavating, hand modeling, and coiling may all be done with the unaided hand, but paddling involves the use of tools. The paddle-and-anvil technique for shaping pottery was known prehistorically. We know this from tools recovered through archeology. Other techniques are represented primarily by their products.

The paddling technique involves forming the plastic clay by hammering on it while the clay is supported from the other side with a hand-held anvil. Some initial forming, by almost any other method, is necessary to provide the cavity in which the anvil is held. The paddle, usually wooden (and rarely recovered archeologically), is beaten against the clay, thinning the clay by squeezing it laterally. The paddle may be carved on its striking surface or have an added covering of cloth, wrapped cord, or matting. The surface relief of the paddle will be reflected on the pot. The anvil is sometimes a suitably shaped smooth stone but more often is itself of pottery (see Figure 49). Ethnographic and archeological records affirm use of the paddle-and-anvil technique in both the Old World (for example, India) and the New World (as in the Mississippi Valley). It has been suggested that some of the alleged anvils recovered archeologically were, in fact, a kind of pottery mold (Foster, 1948).

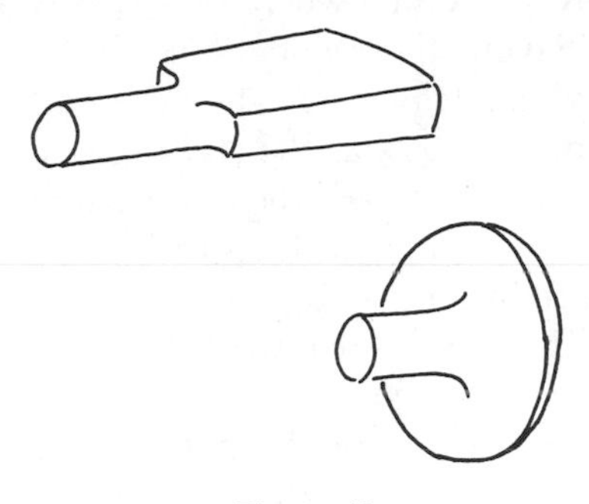

Figure 49

Paddle and anvil

Molding of pottery is divisible into plastic molding and wet molding. In plastic molding, the more common of the two, the soft clay is placed by hand over the surface of a mold (a "male" mold) or inside the cavity of a mold (a "female" mold). Before placing it, the clay may be flattened into a sheet by patting or rolling. It is worked by hand to give an even coverage of the mold with uniform thickness in most areas. Some drying is often allowed before the stiffened clay is slipped from the mold and worked further or is set aside for more drying while the mold is reused. The mold itself is quite variable in nature. The shape, of course, must be that of all or part of the pot form being molded. Materials have included stone, pottery, gourd, basketry, and wood. Some authorities think that early pots were molded in or on baskets, possibly as clay coatings for the baskets rather than as separate vessels in their own right. Pottery fragments (sherds) have been found with basketry impressions. Very few molds for pottery have been identified among archeological remains. Those made of pottery may have been misidentified as thick vessels or their sherds. Most other mold materials are too perishable to have been preserved.

Plastic molded pottery may not be completely formed on or in one mold but may consist of several separately molded pieces joined into one whole. The joints are made by moistening and working the mating edges. With careful work and strategic location at design intersections or certain body points, the joints may not be apparent in the finished product. This makes the detection of the use of molds rather difficult. One possible evidence for molds is the occurrence of pots with identical profiles and other traits reflecting standardization. Yet even some of these characteristics may be the product of templates for modeling rather than the result of molding. However, as with coiled pottery, there may be lines of weakness remaining where the joints were made.

Saving the evidence of the molds themselves, another use of plastic molding leaves no evidence at all. This use of the process involves plastic molded forms as the starting point for further work using the paddle and anvil. As noted above, paddling must start with some semblance of a vessel wall on which to work. The rough, initial form can be easily supplied by a molded product.

If little further work has been done on the molded clay, then some guess may be made as to the type of mold employed. A smooth, even inner surface, or one with a special pattern, will likely result from use of a male mold. If this is true of the outer surface, then a female mold is likely. Whatever the type of mold for plastic molding, it must be shaped so that the clay can be readily removed. No reverse curves should trap the finished work on the mold.

Wet molding is less common among primitives. It is probably an Old World trait which has been introduced in post-Columbian times into the New World. A female (cavity) mold, usually of pottery, is used. A wet slurry of clay is poured into the mold and sloshed around until it deposits a thin coating. Then the remainder of the slurry is poured out. After a brief drying period, the process is repeated and this continues until an adequately thick layer of clay adheres to the mold. Capillary action in the pottery of the mold helps speed the drying of the applied clay. Customarily a group of molds are used at one time and the potter works from one to the next. When the final clay coat is applied, the mold is set aside until the clay has stiffened sufficiently to resist deformation when gently handled. It is then slipped from a one-piece mold; or a two-part mold is opened, and the result removed. From this point on the wet molded clay is treated as though it had been formed by any other technique.

Wet molding can leave telltale lines on the product, reflecting the joints between mold pieces, unless these are burnished off the surface. As with plastic molded pieces several parts may be joined into a larger whole. The lines left by mold-section joints will not be lines of weakness as are the joints between separately molded parts.

Generally, pottery molding, whether plastic or wet, is not very common among more primitive potters. It is usually associated with more advanced groups and with quasi-industrial (quantity) production of pottery. In developmental terms, the next step in complexity of pottery production is the use of the potter's wheel.

The tools of the primitive potter, as used in the techniques discussed above, are quite simple. They consist of some or all of the following: a scraper (of stone, bone, shell, wood); a leathern piece (to smooth wet clay); a pointed tool (bone, wood, antler); and a polisher (pebble). To these simple but effective tools, one must add the fingernails. The paddle and anvil are added for that technique and, of course, molds when pottery is molded.

The tools for decorating pottery include knives and gouges for incising dry or plastic clay, and stamps of wood, stone, shell, or pieces of textile and basketry to be pressed into soft clay. The plastic nature of the clay will facilitate, perhaps encourage or invite, modification of the surface with almost anything which will make an impression. The variable choice for these items makes it difficult to enumerate them as a class, but they are, at the moment, potter's tools.

Potter's Wheel

The development of the potter's wheel may be traced through four stages. The earliest, and not a true wheel, was a hand-rotated platform on which the developing pot was rested. It served primarily as a convenient stand and lacked the lathe-like action of a true potter's wheel. This device, the tournette, probably had its ancestry in a fragment of gourd, a large potsherd, or other base on which the pot was rested while being shaped.

A true potter's wheel, which should be an early form when evaluated on typological grounds, is based on a cart wheel with a platform at the hub to support the pot. Its rim is loaded with clay to enhance the flywheel effect (see Figure 50). The wheel is set in motion by turning it with a stick or directly with the hand. This arrangement is rather awkward for the potter must reach across the flywheel to get at the pot rest. By placing these parts on two different planes, as was done in later wheels, this problem was avoided.

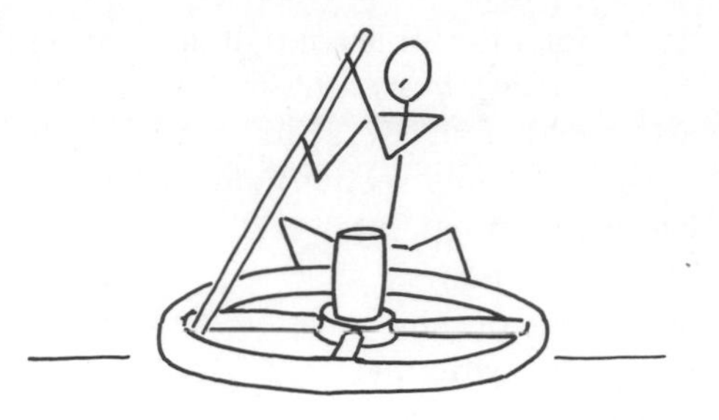

Figure 50

Slow potter's wheel

The "kick wheel" of recent craft potters, widely known in the more sophisticated technologies of Europe, Asia, and North Africa, was recently diffused from Europe to Middle America. The flywheel below and the pot rest above are mounted on a common vertical axle. The potter, seated on a bench facing the wheel, turns it by kicking the flywheel. This organization of parts and their operation makes the tasks of rotating the wheel and forming the pot simultaneous rather than sequential. It also places the pot within convenient reach of the working potter (Figure 51).

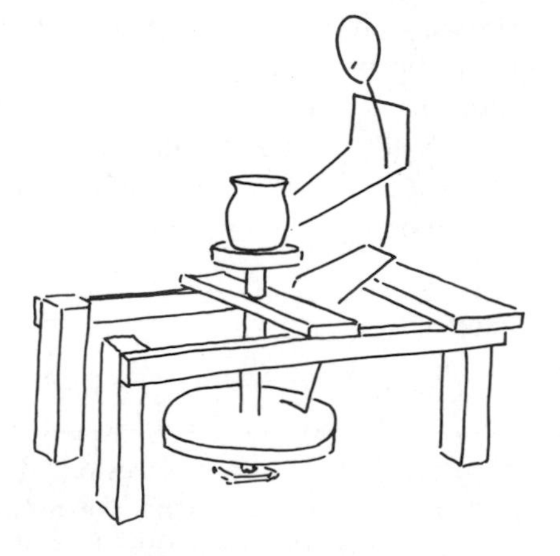

Figure 51

"Kick" wheel

Finally, the foot power applied to the kick wheel was given a slightly different orientation by the introduction of gearing and cranks. A foot treadle to turn the wheel is connected, indirectly, with the pot-supporting portion of the apparatus. The flywheel can be incorporated in the arrangement at any one of several points. With this final refinement, short of being motor driven, the rotation of the wheel is continuous at a substantially constant rate.

The technique of making pots on the wheel is termed "turning" or "throwing." A piece of moist clay is stuck on the turntable and the wheel is set to rotating. The potter primarily uses his hands to shape the clay as the wheel turns. He may check his progress with a template or even use a shaped scraper to give a particular form. When finished the pot is cut loose by drawing a blade or string under it as the wheel continues to turn. Pots thrown on a wheel are characterized by their symmetry about a central axis, and may show even circumferential lines as a resulting of the turning technique. Work on the wheel is quite quick but may be followed by hand modeling to form pouring lips, spouts, handles, lugs, and other asymmetrical parts of the overall design.

Pottery Shapes

The shapes of pottery objects usually are culturally conditioned so that the pottery of each group and time is distinctive. Whenever possible, archeologists rely heavily on this characteristic of ceramic technology for their identification of cultural remains as well as on the material (including temper) and technique of forming.

There are major exceptions to the rule that pottery looks like itself. First, it may be modeled into "effigy" pots, replicas in miniature of real or imaginary creatures, well known in several prehistoric cultures of the Americas — in the Middle Mississippian culture of the Mississippi River drainage, in some central Mexican cultures, and in several Andean cultures. The prehistoric north Chinese made elaborate models of houses and farm scenes in pottery, as did the southeastern Europeans. Such containers used the body or the head of a creature as the main cavity of the vessel. Arms or legs were wrapped around the outside of the body as token representations. Other ceramic pieces were full figures of the object portrayed without any attempt to make containers of them.

The second exception in the appearance of pottery is known as "skeuomorph," or that which is patterned after work in another material. The pottery may retain the shape established by an earlier material, as in the bag-shaped pots known from Neolithic Europe which show the slumping that occurs in old leathern goods, though, of course, nothing comparable occurs in old pottery. Another skeuomorph in pottery is that which imitates a more sophisticated or expensive material. In the Italian Bronze Age there were pottery vessels in imitation of bronze sheet metal containers, presumably for those who could not afford the metal ones.

Generally the skeuomorph is not at all rare and, in fact, seems to be increasingly common in modern times. Imitation leather, complete with scars and branding marks, and plastic molded baskets are two prime examples. An important aspect of the skeuomorph, beyond its shape, is that the limitations of the original material as they influence surface treatment, freedom of manipulation, or any other technical requirement, are carried over into the new material for which they are not relevant. It is this as much as shape transfer which creates the category.

Ornamentation

Surface treatment of pottery, which is as varied as is shape, is also a culturally conditioned feature used by archeologists to identify cultures and cultural influences. The simplest treatment of pottery surfaces is to do nothing at all. A texture may be provided, perhaps inadvertently, by work marks. An example is found in the thumbnail-impressed utilitarian wares of the Anasazi tradition in the American Southwest. These show the marks of the thumbnail as it was used to press the coils of the pot together.

Though a surface can be smoothed so as to present no great textural differences between one part and another, it may show different colors due to firing conditions. An area may show a lighter or darker tone where flame or smoke struck it; this condition is sometimes called "flame-spotting" or a "smoke cloud." Though it can occur accidentally, the marking is sometimes induced.

Additions to the surface of the pottery may include a slip or wash, encrustations, relief modeling (negative as well as positive), glazes, and paints.

The slip is a fine layer of clay applied in a fluid state to the surface of the pot. It may be added by dipping the vessel or, for the interior, by pouring the slip into and then out of the vessel. The slip must undergo a firing and is noticeable as a distinct layer in a cross section of the vessel wall. If the slip does not cover the entire available surface, it is said to be "reserved." The areas slipped produce a decorative contrast in color or texture with the paste of the pot.

Encrustation on pots are usually of stone and metal. For this reason their attachment and retention are difficult due to differential expansion coefficients which cause many encrustations to pop off or explode when the vessel is fired. To avoid this the stones and metal are held loosely in a bezel-like setting so that they may expand and contract independently during the firing process.

Relief modeling of a pot may involve nothing more than relief ornament in the plastic paste of the vessel. However, rather substantial designs can be made by the attachment of buttons, rolls, and other separate pieces of clay which adhere and are ultimately baked in place by firing. Negative relief may be produced by excavating portions of the paste, a removal rather than an addition, but nevertheless related.

Glazes are a special thing for potters. Some authorities hold that the only true glazes are those which, basically, are glass, made from some form of silica and colored by metal oxides. If this rigid definition is accepted, then glazes occur only in the Old World. The glaze, added after the first firing of the pottery (which resulted in "bisque" or "biscuit ware"), must itself be fired at high temperatures. The materials are literally melted into a glassy, impervious coating on the pot.

So-called false glazes, made from various alkaline salts, lead salts ("plumbate" glazes), and feldspar, were used in the Meso-American civilizations. It is noteworthy that all glazing, however defined, is limited to more sophisticated peoples.

Because the color of glazes and paints as they are prepared only remotely approximates their color after they have been fired, each new paint or glaze undergoes considerable experimentation to determine its ultimate color. For this reason, a formula, once derived, is likely to be closely followed thereafter.

Paints can be applied either to the initially dried clay or to the bisque state (once fired). In the former instance the paint will, of course, be fired along with the paste. In the latter case the painted bisque may be refired, but not necessarily. If the paint isn't fired onto the paste, then it may prove a bit temporary. Unfired paints, which may wash off pot sherds, are often called "fugitive" by archeologists. Like surface modeling, the painting, and even glazing, of surfaces may be negative or reserved. The design which is emphasized is untouched while the background gets the color.

The plasticity of clay lends itself to still other surface treatments. Those mentioned above were for the most part added to the dried (leather state) clay; those which follow are done to the still plastic paste. Textile or cord impression, mentioned briefly in the paddle-and-anvil technique, was widely used for ornament but fell out of favor among more advanced peoples. This simple ornamentation may have originated accidentally as the fresh clay pot was marked by a basket or cloth on which it rested. The result was approved and later done deliberately. Cord marking was likely done with a cord held taut between the hands. Cord- or textile-wrapped paddles or sticks were used to mark soft clay surfaces even when they did not play a part in pot shaping. In addition to reflecting a cultural practice related to pottery ornamentation, studies made of cord- or textile-marking have shed light on some textile work of the past, since the impression in pottery is far more permanent than the perishable original (Rachlin, 1955).

Punctation and noding are a pair of opposed techniques for ornamenting pottery. Punctations are depressions put into the surface from outside, usually with a simple tool. Noding is the reverse, with a lump raised on the outside by pressing on the plastic clay from within the vessel.

Stamping in plastic clay has many variations, from a simple punctation to elaborate patterns approaching block prints. Stamps themselves can be simple patterns cut in the end of a stick, a semicircular rocker stamp, or a little wheel ("roulette") with a patterned edge.

Finally, without exhausting the possibilities, polishing may be mentioned. The rubbing to polish a surface may be applied at almost any stage in manufacture — on the dried clay, on the bisque, over paint, even on twice-fired ware. Polishing may pattern the surface by "reserving" a part of the design field, that is, leaving it unpolished. At whatever stage the polishing is applied one may be reasonably certain that it is not over a glaze and that it is the final step in surface treatment.

Firing and Kilns

Firing, the step which converts clay into pottery or ceramic ware, is, of course, vital to the whole process. Despite its importance, firing can be a very simple, casual process, which may take no more than an hour.

Firing exposes the clay to such heat as will drive off the water of hydration. The heat may additionally vitrify the glaze. There are two crude techniques of firing which do not require any kiln or oven. In one technique a pot or pile of pots is surrounded by a ring of fuel which is set ablaze; in the other, the situation is reversed with the fire surrounded by stacked pots. For good results in either instance the fire should not touch the pot; to do so would cause undesirable marks. It may be supposed that the fire-ring will provide the more even heat. It is also easier to tend and refuel. In practice the fire is often allowed to burn fiercely and then die down, for the fuels used — light brush, animal dung, and twigs — usually burn quickly with a hot fire.

Proper kilns for firing pottery have two chambers which separate the fire from the pots. The hot gases pass from the fire box to heat the pots before being vented to the air. A kiln requires longer heating and cooling time and more substantial fuels than an open fire does, but it also permits much greater control of the whole firing process. The heat generated is contained around the pots; the temperature and duration of heat are better determined; and the nature of the atmosphere within the kiln can be changed to suit the occasion. The presence or absence of oxygen and carbon compounds in the kiln gases affect the color of the paste, the paints, and the glazes. The clays contain, among other things, iron and alumina which respond to being heated in an oxidizing (oxygen-rich) or reducing (carbon-rich) atmosphere. The resulting pastes are in the brown-yellow-orange-red range or the black-gray-white range, respectively. Paints and glazes, when they contain other metallic elements, show other results. A given kiln can, during one firing, have both types of atmosphere present successively to produce, for example, a gray smudge on a reddish paste. However, since this entire topic is still under investigation by those concerned with primitive ceramics, it would be premature to consider the present evaluations conclusive.

Kilns generally are used by the more sophisticated, full-time potters. Domestic potters often get along without a permanent or elaborate kiln.

A final note should be made regarding potters. When pottery was a domestic craft among nonliterates, it was usually the work of women, with each meeting the needs of her household. When potting became one of the first craft specializations, men predominated as full-time potters, and women assumed a subordinate role. In virtually all native instances of wheel-made pottery the potter's wheel is the tool of men.

13

Leather

Hides, the raw material of furs and leather, have been with us since man killed his first food animal. Early man must have used some of these hides for clothing, bedding, housing, or parts of artifacts (skin bags, lashings, drum heads, and so on). The material was at hand, and the needs everpresent. However, we do not know what steps these men took to preserve the hides or furs, to make them supple, or to convert them to the moment's needs. The only thing of which we can be reasonably certain is that hides were utilized as sheet materials before such materials were created through weaving techniques.

The Upper Paleolithic remains in Europe reveal examples of needles and awls. The former are construed as evidence for the sewing of skins — a view supported by other alleged parallels between the cultures of this time and place and some cultures of the circumpolar zone (for example, the Chukchi of northeastern Siberia, the Lapps of Scandinavia, and the Eskimo). It is supposed that the skills necessary to weave textiles, the alternative material, came much later. We find, of course, a loose association between cloth weaving and the Neolithic subsistence style.

Tanning is the generic term for the preservation of hides and their conversion to leather. Correctly, tanning is only one of several techniques for this purpose. However, the word will be used here in the common sense, rather than technically.

Fur dressing is the proper term for the treatment of a skin "in the hair." When it is desired that the hair be kept then some stringent limitations must be placed on the procedures for preservation. Scraping is limited to one side (and gently at that), the chemical agents used must not loosen the hair, and the skin usually cannot be split. The result on furs is often less complete than on leather so that a later wetting will cause stiffening when dry and possibly result in spoilage. In general fur dressing is characterized by fewer steps and more limited means than leather tanning.

The entire tanning process passes through three major steps — dehairing, scraping, tanning — which may be facilitated by the addition of other intermediate steps.

Before a skin can be tanned it must be removed from the animal. Only with smaller animals is skinning commonly done with a knife. Larger ones often have the skin loosened by pounding with a hammer or flail. The skin can then be pulled off with a minimum of cutting. Some animals are skinned with the hide almost intact, as a sort of bag, by turning the skin inside out from one end. A hide handled in this fashion lends itself to certain forms of tannage to be mentioned below.

The first treatment of the skin is washing and pounding it to clean away dirt, blood, and some excess flesh. Once called "stocking," the pounding process, which loosens the fibers and makes the skin more receptive to the chemicals which follow, was one of the first tanning processes to be mechanized. In fourteenth-century Europe water mills drove drop hammers — stocking machines — which pounded wet hides. At a later date these were replaced by revolving drums in which hides were placed to be pummelled or "drummed."

Dehairing can be done in a number of ways. In fact it is difficult not to have some hair fall out when engaged in fur dressing. A simple dehairing technique is "sweating," an induced, controlled rotting of the hide, under conditions of warmth and high humidity. Urine can be used to soak the hides during this stage as it dehairs and swells the skin. Liming will do the same thing and probably derives from earlier use of wood ashes. Recent practice calls for the use of lime solutions of progressively greater strength. Fresh, strong solutions are added, and the spent solutions, into which the hide is first placed, are discarded. A similar rotation of solutions, of graded strengths, is found in the tanning processes themselves.

Scraping or "beaming" hides actually removes the hair loosened by sweating or liming. The hide is placed over a beam (perhaps a longitudinal third of a log), pegged on the ground, or stretched on a frame. There it is scraped on the hair side to remove the hair and on the flesh side to remove subcutaneous tissue and fat. Hammering with a series of glancing blows may also be used to remove the hair through a kind of plucking action. What remains after scraping is the corium layer of the skin, with the epidermal and subcutaneous layers removed.

If the hair is to remain on the skin, the skin is scraped only on the flesh side. Care must be taken on thin skins not to scrape too hard and cut into the bases of the hair follicles which would cause the hairs to be drawn through to the wrong side of the skin. A dull scraper, which has no shaving action, will probably prevent this damage.

The scrapers used in this step are highly variable in form and material. They certainly included the stone endscrapers recovered in such numbers from some archeological contexts. Slate scrapers were of the same form as the semicircular metal knife of later leather workers. Bone scrapers included some tibiae, scapulae, and ribs. The tibia has a straight scraping edge. The scapula, equipped with a handle, was used as a form of spade thrust forward over the hide. The rib worked well on the convex surface of a beam. The moon knife ("lunette") in metal was a favorite of medieval tanners.

Scraping is followed by washing to remove the traces of dehairing agents. Lime-dissolving materials may be used to neutralize the lime, if any. Recently acids were used for this purpose; anciently sugar, honey, and sour milk were used. The deliming process may be accompanied by more scraping, the whole known as "scudding." The hides may be swelled again ("plumped") by this washing process, sometimes aided by the application of bird manure or dog dung. Plumping and liming assist the uptake of tannins, but they do not have much value when mineral or oil tannage is used.

Tanning Methods

There are three principal tanning methods, each best suited to the production of leather for certain uses, and each involving a different group of agents: oil or fat tannage, mineral tannage, and vegetable tanning. The preparation for each method is slightly different; that described above is best adapted to vegetable tanning. There are, however, many tanners who use combined tans which have elements from two or more of these general approaches.

Oil Tannage. Oil or fat tannage is also known as chamois dressing or wash leather dressing. The derivation of "chamois" is obscure; there probably is no connection with the animal of that name. The wash leather designation is more to the point because the products are washable, soft, tough and much preferred for clothing because they will not become stiff through wetting. The process is likely quite old, at least as part of a combined tan.

The scraped, clean hide is saturated with oil, worked (stocked) with wooden spades, kneaded (pummelled or trampled), and spread in the sun. This sequence is repeated many times until the skin will absorb no more oil. Finally the hide is worked back and forth over a blunt-ended stake ("staked") until it is soft and flexible.

Brain currying, which was common among North American Indians, is a part of oil tannage. The brains contain fat and an emulsifier which is worked into the skin. Brains may be used in conjunction with a smoke tan, and their action in this case is probably limited to lubricating the tanned hide.

The oiling (stuffing, feeding) of semifinished leathers is necessary to restore the oils lost in the washing and tanning processes and to make the leather flexible. A leather which lacks these oils is called "empty" and is stiff and dry. Obviously, the oil tanning process does two steps in one, and its products do not need final oiling along with staking.

The chewing of hides is primarily useful for its mechanical action in bending stiffened fibers. Any tanning effect comes through the emulsifying power of the saliva which will dissolve available fats and enable them to enter the hide. In this fashion the hide might be oil tanned with its own residual fat or even with grease or oil rubbed off its human user. The use of chewed reindeer liver as a tanning agent is utilization of this emulsifying action. So each time some dutiful Eskimo wife chews her husband's stiff leather clothing or his boots she may be reducing her future labor by adding a bit of an oil tan.

Mineral Tanning. Mineral tanning is often called tawing when alum is involved. By itself alum produces a stiff, empty leather which requires much subsequent working to soften. Therefore, alum tans are rarely used today though alum may figure in a combined tan.

A simple fur dressing is primarily an alum tan. The flesh side of the skin is treated with alum and salt. The hides are stacked, flesh-to-flesh, in a cool place for several days. Upon removal they are scraped, stretched, pulled, and rubbed into a final soft state. A problem with the alum tan is that it is not quite complete and can be reversible in the presence of moisture. This explains why the thorough wetting of furs is so disastrous, and why damp furs smell so much like a wet dog. They have not been converted thoroughly to another material.

The acute stiffness of an alum tan is slightly alleviated by the addition of salt. When possible, some oil is used to finish the leather. The oil can appear in the process as part of a combined tan, such as one which uses a paste of alum, salt, egg yolk, flour, and oil. After thorough saturation the hides are hung for several weeks, then dampened and trampled before they are finally staked.

There is another tan, possibly introduced to eastern Europe from central Asia, which combines two mineral tans with oil. The hide is initially tawed with alum. It is then stuffed with hot beef tallow and finally stretched over a coal fire to burn in the fat. The coal fire emits tars and other products which have additional tanning powers. These are comparable to a modern formaldehyde tan.

Smoke tanning is basically a mineral tan capable of being complete in itself, but it is frequently combined with oil or vegetable tans. Smoke usually follows oil or fat but precedes a vegetable tan. Many tanning processes are very slow, but smoke tanning can be quite quick. Exposure to smoke for an hour, followed by burial in a pit for a day, may be adequate. Some Asiatic peoples were reported to use this process at a quasi-industrial level in the hands of fulltime tanners. There is a suggestion that smoke tanning may be one of the circumpolar traits, having had its origin in northern Asia and been diffused to northern North America.

Vegetable Tanning. Vegetable tanning is, for the purist, the only true tan because it involves the use of tannins. Possible tanning agents, used directly or in solution, include: oak bark (tan bark), oak galls, sumac, catechol (an acacia resin), acacia pods, pomegranate rinds, chestnut wood, pine bark, and grape juice. Solutions of tanning agents (tan liquors) are used in successively stronger concentrations with the hides soaked for weeks or months in each. The usual container is a pit or tub, but a variant exists in bottle- or bag-tannage. The skin (flesh side out) is sewn into a bag which is filled with tanning liquor or a direct tanning agent (leaves, bark). The bag is then hung in a water- or liquor-filled pit or simply in the open air for months. Skin which has been removed from the animal by peeling lends itself very well to this method.

When the hides are treated with direct tanning agents, used in substantially dry forms, they are piled in layers alternately with the agent in a damp pit. Weighted down with stones, the hides may be left untouched for more than a year.

Vegetable tans may be combined with other tans, especially chemical ones. Tanning and tawing (alum tan) can be applied successively to the same hide. Usually the hide is stored for a while between the two processes to let the first treatment have maximum effect. The order in which the two processes are used is related to the character of the leather with which one finishes; as the final step tanning produces a tougher, stiffer leather than does tawing.

Whether alone or with mineral tans, the vegetable tanned product requires stuffing (oiling) to make it usable. It is kneaded and worked, possibly staked, in this last step.

Finishing Leathers

The splitting or shaving of leathers is generally not characteristic of their treatment by more primitive peoples. One can surmise that they were able to select a skin at the outset which would finish with the desired characteristics. As populations grew and man became more dependent upon domesticated animals for his needs, there was a narrowing of the range of choice along with an increasing need for leather. The hides of relatively few kinds of animals, the domesticates, had to serve many purposes. Splitting leathers is one way in which a thin leather can be obtained from a thick hide. If a skin is split into two pieces, a simple thing for thick hides, then the amount of available leather has been doubled. Also the split hide produces pieces of differing qualities — in general, the outside portion is preferred. Leather splitting requires sharp knives and a steady hand. It also calls for another finishing step — burnishing. A smooth, hard polisher is rubbed over the split surface of the leather to produce a finish somewhat comparable to the outer surface of the skin.

Finally, many leathers are dyed or painted before or after their manufacture into finished goods. This "improvement" on nature is as characteristic of so-called primitives as it is of more industrialized peoples. If the natural colors were the sole possibilities, then the results would be rather drab. As it is, some leathers resemble anything but the original hide when they have been completely processed.

Rawhide

There is one hide product to which virtually none of the foregoing applies — rawhide. This is not a leather, but simply a scraped, untanned hide. It might seem that failure to tan the hide would be courting trouble, but the result is another material with its own merits and uses. Rawhide, kept dry, lasts very well, and it can be returned to a soft, pliable state by wetting. Care must be taken, however, that moisture does not persist or the hide will rot.

Fresh or damp rawhide can be molded into elaborate shapes over sand or clay cores. On drying it becomes very rigid, and the core can be broken out to leave a cavity. The object — a container, a mask, an ornament — can be painted.

Rawhide is a prime material for lashings. While soft it can be drawn around the members to be joined. On drying it pulls taut and hardens into a very tough, semiflexible fastening. It can hold some things together, for example a stone blade to a wooden handle, in a fashion that few other materials can match.

Thinking back to the consideration of materials and fastenings, it is interesting to consider a carefully designed structure of bamboo fastened with rawhide. It is one with great potentialities for strength combined with light weight. Though basically a primitive structure, it may well match some of the better modern ones.

Social Organization of Tanners

Tanning has its spatial and social aspects. In general, it is a domestic craft conducted close to home. Women are most often the tanners among nonliterates, and they combine this work with other domestic occupations. The demands of child-rearing and the intermittent nature of many activities preclude the establishment of work places at a distance. Only the need for quantities of water might tend to override these considerations.

As the occupation of full-time specialists, tanning comes to be viewed in a different light and is often banished from the settlement or relegated to its outskirts. Tanneries were often located on streams, and one might even imagine that some people were so squeamish as to insist that the tannery be downstream of the principal watering point. It might also be advantageous for the tannery to be on the opposite side of the community from the prevailing wind. The tanners probably kept company in their workplaces with dyers and bleachers.

When tanning is a domestic art, it is hardly possible to set apart from the rest of the society those who are so engaged. Female relatives — wives, mothers, sisters — can be expected to object to ostracism stemming from the practice of a housewifely task. By contrast, or perhaps when inclination is given free rein, the full-time specialist tanner is likely to occupy a low social status. The job itself is unpleasant and malodorous. The tanner uses materials such as urine and dog dung, the collection of which is often highly public but not highly regarded. The tanner and his possessions become impregnated with the elements of his work. He may be unwelcome company for this, if for no other reason. There is also an important reason for the low estate of tanners in some societies. In the value systems of these cultures, as in southern Asia, the tanner is ritually unclean because of his association with the processing of animal products. He is a colleague of the slaughterer and the butcher; he profits from the taking of animal life. Defiled himself, the tanner is capable of transmitting this ritual contagion to others. Consequently, where the society is stratified on the basis of ritual cleanliness in relation to occupation, the tanner is in the lower classes.

It would appear that, historically, the tanners were once lumped in stratified societies with other industrial workers with hides. The leather workers — harness, shoe, and garment makers — were part of the same group. As time passed and specialization grew, the leather workers drew themselves away from the tanners. Some of the leather workers, in the more specialized branches (such as glovers), set themselves apart from the rest. So there resulted a hierarchy of groups working with hides and leather, but the tanner always remained near the bottom of the system. If any generalization can be hazarded about this situation, it is that the more highly processed the leather became and the more it diverged from the original hide, the more elevated was the social status of its workers.

The production of leather has not yielded much to modern industrial processes with the result that it has become comparatively expensive. There is a great deal of direct hand labor involved in tanning. It is, of course, the use of machines which reduces the cost of goods in the industrial system.

This situation and the increased production of synthetic materials mean that leather is, proportionately, rarer today than it was in the past. Plastic sheet materials have come to displace leather in many uses: upholstery, clothing, luggage, covers, cases, and even footgear. Nonetheless, leather retains a strong appeal for certain consumers who are willing to pay a premium for the advantages of the material or for its status value. Despite the considerable advances in the physical characteristics of plastic substitutes, leather will remain with us for some years to come.

14

Metallurgy

Metallurgy depends upon the ability to smelt ores into metal. The term, however, is often broadened to include the working of metal using heat. We will employ the term in this broader sense.

Metals found in nature in the metallic state rather than as ores were used by primitive men long before the art of smelting was mastered. Gold and silver occur in nugget form, as does copper. Native gold and silver were used in many parts of the world where the metals were found, but they did not, in themselves, give any marked stamp to a culture. Native or "float" copper, on the other hand, was the basis for substantial developments in the upper Mississippi River valley. The Old Copper Culture made use of the metal, nonmetallurgically it would seem, to produce tools, weapons, and ornaments (Martin, et al., 1947:299). Gold and silver were used for little more than ornaments, and copper artifacts, however useful, were a bit soft, but premetallurgical iron was known and worked. This iron was rare, coming from meteorites (an unreliable source at best), but greatly appreciated. In fact, the meteoric metal was of far better quality, being a nickel steel, than men were able to smelt before recent historic times.

Iron of this nonmetallurgical sort made a great deal of difference to the Eskimo of Greenland, Ellsmere, and Baffin Lands who exploited an iron meteorite of many tons' weight. It had been worked smooth, with all projections broken off, before it was moved in this century to the American Museum of Natural History in New York. Rarely does a museum capture in its entirety an aboriginal iron "mine."

These nonmetallurgical approaches to metals were based upon their treatment as malleable stones. The bits were hammered, broken, and ground into shape. Iron pieces were so small and rare that they were used only for crucial parts of artifacts, and small, sharp pieces were set into handles in the style of the microliths of Mesolithic times.

Whatever the technical limitations in handling these metals it was recognized that they were something extraordinary. Some became valued as precious metals. Utilitarian considerations gave copper and allied metals (tin, antimony, arsenic, zinc) their worth. Iron, possibly because of its ore magnetite (the lodestone) and possibly because of its sometime extraterrestrial origin, was held in special esteem as having magical powers. In time a considerable folklore has built up around the metals.

Metallurgy in the proper sense had two origins according to our present understanding. One of these, responsible for Old World developments in all metals, lay in the Near Eastern-Anatolian area. The other, of which we are less sure, probably originated in Peru and gave rise to limited nonferrous metallurgy in the New World (Willey, 1955:584). While particular traits and achievements may mark developments in this region or that, ultimately the ideas are traceable back to these two places. There is at present no known prehistoric connection between the metallurgies of the two hemispheres.

The dating of these events is more uncertain than their location. In part this uncertainty arises from the sparseness of evidence and the gradual acquisition of the art. In the Near East copper was in use by 6000 B.C. with some assurance of the use of heat a millenium later and smelting by 4000 B.C. (Wertime, 1964:1259). By 3500 B.C. metals had a substantial impact on the cultures of the Near East and were spreading outward in all directions. In the New World metallurgical developments started between 750 B.C. and the beginning of the Christian era. Some problems of dating are coupled, in this estimate, with little assurance that all the evidence has been gathered. A rapid northward spread toward Middle America, however, seems certain.

The limits of prehistoric diffusion of metal in the Old World were quite broad. Virtually all peoples of Eurasia used metal before the advent of history. Only the most primitive of Africans — the Pygmies and the Bushmen — did not do their own ironworking. Southeast Asian metallurgy, itself of probable Indian origin, spread over Indonesia. Beyond there, however, there are only sporadic hints of metal-using peoples in western New Guinea and then nothing more to be found in the Oceanic area or in Australia.

In the New World metal was confined to the area between central Mexico and Bolivia or northern Chile. To the north of this region there were only the uses of native metals discussed earlier, strictly nonmetallurgical, it would seem. Further it should be noted that the metallurgists of the New World made no use of iron but stayed with the silver-gold-copper-tin group. These softer metals were used more for ornaments than for tools so the cultural consequences of a Metal Age were different in this hemisphere.

Mining

Because metallurgy includes the ability to smelt metals from ores, one must start with the ores at the mines. We have no sure way of knowing how the first smelters became aware of the relation between ores and metals, since they bear little resemblance to one another. Further, a given metal may come from a number of ores, each quite different in appearance. Whatever it was that directed the attention of early metallurgists, they obtained their ores from the surface. Open pit mining was the most common form employed, but veins of ore were followed for short distances into the earth.

Mining was not far different from the quarrying which had been a part of stoneworking. Ores were dug out with many of the same tools: antler picks and rakes, stone mauls, scapula hoes. Few metal tools were used until iron became abundant; tools made of softer metals were ineffective and the later, better metals were needed initially for such important purposes as weapons. Techniques such as fire-setting and wedging were used to crack and loosen the ore bodies.

Open pit mines, found worldwide, were extensively used in prehistoric Africa in those same areas noted today for mining. That many of the African pits have been backfilled has puzzled some observers. It is suggested here that the entire pit was never open at one time, but that the mining proceeded as a trench moving laterally. This explanation is supported by the Africans' motor habits using the hoe, their common digging tool. The user stoops over, chops away in front of himself, and throws the earth back past his legs. In this fashion the ore would be collected and removed in baskets, and the waste thrown behind to "backfill" the pit (Cline, 1937:57).

The habit of following ore veins downward from the surface led to the digging of bell-shaped pits — shafts which were widened below ground level to maximize ore recovery. Such pits, due to their undercuts, were hazardous to miners and to the general public; people or animals who tumbled in could not get out without help (Salzman, 1923:7).

Because there was no sure way of locating totally buried mineral deposits, though dowsing was employed in medieval times, shaft-and-gallery mining came later and was not generally found among primitives. Only the richest ore deposits were exploited, in part because there was no pressure to use low grade ores, and in part because the smelting processes would not handle any but the highest grades.

The expansion of mining and smelting led to serious deforestation in some areas as trees were cut to provide timbering for the mines to prevent collapse of extensively excavated chambers. Had the miners been content to remove less ore there would have been less need for pit props. Wood was also needed to make the charcoal with which smelting was conducted. Until the development of new techniques it was not possible to substitute coal for this purpose.

Once excavated the ores were crushed and washed. Panning was employed, for example in Africa and South America, to concentrate the metallic ores. The greater weight of the metalliferous portion caused it to remain in the pan while the lighter impurities floated away. Though mining was usually done by men, women and children joined in the transporting and cleaning of ores.

Smelting

Smelting was generally done by reduction of metallic oxides in a furnace. Hot gases containing carbon combined with the oxides to carry off the oxygen in carbon monoxide and dioxide compounds. If the ore to be smelted was not an oxide, but a carbonate or sulfide of the metal, then it might be subjected to preliminary roasting to convert it to that form. Roasting was done in the open air by piling the ores on a large fire.

The charge of a smelting furnace consisted of layers of fuel (usually charcoal) and ore, with the possible inclusion of a limestone or other flux which would combine readily with impurities and hold them separate from the fluid metal. Once these materials had been placed in the furnace, it was set afire, the draft adjusted to produce a proper blaze, and the whole thing tended for hours or even days until combustion-reduction was complete. Though fuel, flux, or even ore might be added during this time, none of the primitive smelters ran on a continuous production basis. Ultimately the fire died down, the furnace opened to let out the slag, and finally the metal removed from the very bottom. The furnace was then cleaned, possibly repaired, and recharged for another run. Production from such operations must have been low by modern standards. Recent efforts to bolster the Chinese economy through the encouragement of similar crude smelters seems to have netted no more than twenty-five tons of iron per smelter annually. The size of pre- and protohistoric metal hoards suggests that early figures were even smaller.

Primitive furnaces ranged from simple pits to elaborately equipped structures. The pits were rare because they worked rather poorly; most were about two to three feet in diameter and in depth. Some had draft-inducing auxiliaries, discussed below. The most common furnace was one built on top of the ground and about the same size as the pit furnace. Some of the large African furnaces were made by eviscerating ant hills.

Figure 52

Types of African furnaces

The tightly cemented walls withstood heat well and could be used repeatedly. The taller furnaces, ten or more feet high, sometimes had sheds or roofs built around them to shelter the work crew during the long hours when it was necessary to stay with the lighted furnace. The ground level furnace had a trench dug into its base into which the slag could run (Figure 52).

Bellows

The draft for the furnace was more commonly forced than natural, though some arrangements relied on prevailing winds. The pit or trench furnace had a trench directed from its base into the wind in an effort to fan the fire. A hillside furnace is known which had a tunnel funneling the wind into the lower part of the furnace. Neither of these arrangements is as reliable as an artificial draft furnished by bellows.

The many types of bellows used in furnaces and forges doubtless supplanted the use of fans and the blowpipe in some cultures. New World cultures do not seem to have had indigenous bellows. The bag bellows (Figure 53) is one of the simplest, and possibly oldest, patterns. A bag has one end arranged so that it may be opened and closed by the hand of the operator. The other end is fastened to a tube leading to the fire. As the operator raises the bag, he opens the top so that it may fill with air, then squeezes the top closed and presses down to force the air out the other end into the tube. This style of bellows, the most widespread form of the device, was known in the Old World from southern Asia across the Near East into Europe and into much of SubSaharan Africa. Derived from it is the concertina bellows which uses a rigid base and a series of internal rings to hold a longer bag in shape. The valving is still handled through the top. Bellows of the type recently common in western Europe are evidently derived from the concertina type and so ultimately from the bag bellows.

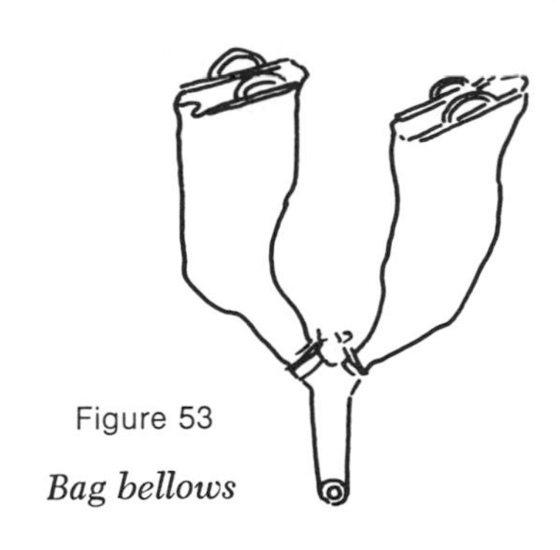

Figure 53

Bag bellows

The SubSaharan Africans made considerable use of several varieties of pot or drum bellows which consist of a base chamber of wood or pottery to the top of which is fastened a loose diaphragm of leather. In the center of the diaphragm is a loop or stick handle by which the operator raises and lowers the skin. This bellows obviously lacks a valving system, but it operates effectively by reason of its use with a Venturi tube. The air expelled by the bellows draws free air through the Venturi tube toward the fire. When the diaphragm rises and draws air through the outlet tube, most of the intake air comes from free air rather than back through the Venturi tube (see Figure 54).

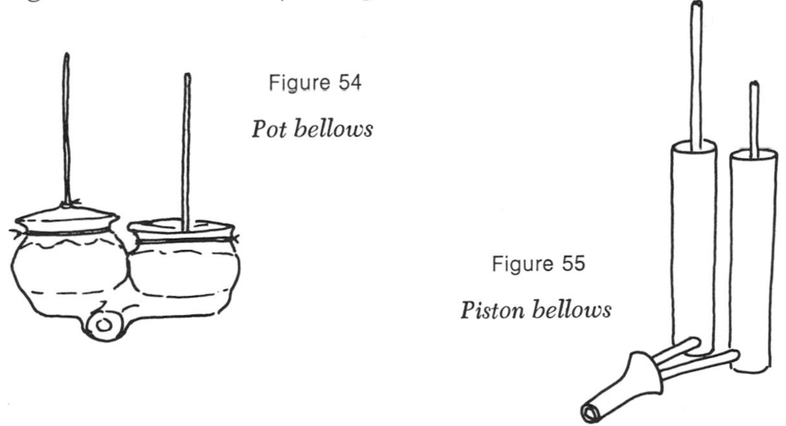

Figure 54

Pot bellows

Figure 55

Piston bellows

In the Southeast Asian culture sphere the common type was the piston bellows (Figure 55). A loosely fitting piston runs in a vertical tube, with a cloth or feather edging forming a seal to the inside of the cylinder.

As the piston is raised the seal collapses inward permitting air to pass to the underside of the piston. On the downstroke the seal is pressed outward against the cylinder wall and the air is forced out the bottom of the cylinder into a tube leading to the fire. The valving system is virtually the same as that on our present day tire pump.

Bag bellows, the derivative concertina bellows, pot or drum bellows, and piston bellows were usually operated in pairs. The smelter's or smith's assistant operated one of the pair with each hand. For a forge a pair usually sufficed, but a smelter's furnace might need several pairs. The tube through which the air is carried into the fire is known as a tuyère. Tuyères, with or without forced draft, are commonly used in multiples.

Figure 56

Box bellows

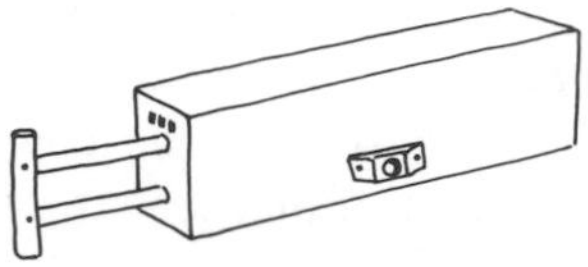

In the Far East — China and Japan — is found the box bellows (Figure 56) which is far more sophisticated than any type mentioned above, even more than the European bellows. The box bellows consists of a long rectangular-sectioned chamber (the cylinder) in which there is set a movable partition (the piston) dividing the chamber end from end. Each end wall has an intake valve and in the side wall near each end is a port communicating to a passage located alongside the main chamber. At the midpoint of this passage is a lateral outlet with a swinging valve which alternately blocks one end of the passage to prevent the exiting air from recycling to the other end of the cylinder. The piston is mounted on the end of two parallel shafts which protrude through the end wall of the cylinder. A crosshandle gives the operator his grip. As the piston is moved in the cylinder, air is forced alternately from the ends of the cylinder. This double-acting air pump is used singly to supply draft to a furnace or forge (Hommel, 1937:18).

Techniques of Metalworking

The techniques of metalworking differed according to the metal being used and the results desired.

Cold hammering was widely used with the more ductile metals such as gold and silver. It could be pursued with other nonferrous metals, but continued working made copper and bronze brittle. If the desired shape was not achieved before embrittlement, then the metal was annealed by heating and rapid cooling. It is possible that annealing was the first use made of heat in the whole metallurgical complex, preceding smelting or welding.

Hot forging of metals became much more common when iron came into use, since only a limited amount of cold working of steels can be done. Heating, followed by slow cooling, annealed steels; rapid quenching of the heat made steels harder, tempered them.

Most iron used by man is actually alloyed into steel of some sort. When iron ores are smelted with carbon fuels, the carbon in the furnace combines with the product to make a steel. Mild steels, which we commonly refer to as iron, have 0.05 percent to 0.30 percent of carbon. Steel for today's tools runs about 0.75 percent to 1.0 percent carbon, while very hard items like files run to 1.25 percent carbon. (Other metals are additionally alloyed in modern steels.) Since the differences in carbon content between some radically different kinds of steel are quite small, the metallurgist must exercise careful control. Evidently primitive smelting was at times a rather hit-and-miss affair.

Since most primitive furnaces were not capable of very high temperatures, they did not produce quantities of molten iron. Instead the iron formed as droplets, so-called point melting, in the furnace and trickled down to form a spongy mass, the bloom, in the base of the furnace. After the smelting process had run its course, the bloom was dragged from the furnace and possibly broken into smaller pieces. This metal was heated and hammered repeatedly to control the quantity and distribution of carbon which, depending upon the treatment, could be added or removed at this step. But for most nonliterates, the low furnace temperatures precluded the casting of iron into molds.

The drawing of wire is basically a forging process even though it is done cold among simpler peoples. A rod of metal was hammered down at one end until it would pass through a hole in a drawplate or die. The reduced end was held in a clamp and the rod pulled through the hole by force. The process was repeated, using successively smaller holes in the drawplate, until the intended wire size was reached. Drawing was done best with the more ductile metals, but others could be annealed between passes through the die. Various kinds of levers and simple windlasses were devised to supply the considerable force necessary. Wire drawing was known in SubSaharan Africa and in a belt from Europe across southern Asia to the Far East (Figure 57).

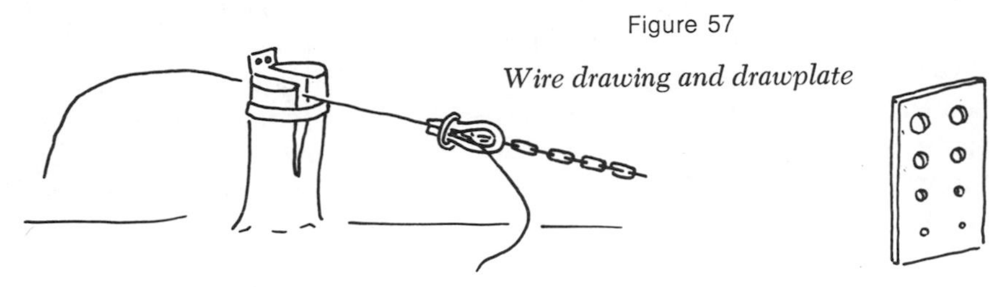

Figure 57

Wire drawing and drawplate

Casting

The casting of metals was a widespread technique with several methods known in both Old and New Worlds. The nonferrous metals lent themselves well to casting, but, as noted above, iron casting was late and restricted.

The simplest kind of casting is done into an open mold to form ingots (some used for money), rods, and more elaborate shapes. Some open molds were simply earth cavities, but others were formed in clay or cut in stone. The stone molds, usually in soft limestone or steatite, could produce castings of some detail and precision. The open side of the mold left the casting unfinished on that surface, so some later finishing was necessary. Many ornaments, such as brooches, buckles, even bracelets, may be made in this fashion.

An elaboration of the open mold involved the addition of a flat cover to close the open side. While this does no more than confine the molten metal and control the ultimate thickness, the addition necessitated passages for the admission of the metal and vents to purge the evolved gases. The closed mold raises problems of premature chilling of the metal and resultant incomplete filling, but preliminary heating of the mold reduces the heat loss and aids the flow.

Split molds are closed molds with a part of the casting cavity in each mold section. Often the molds are in two pieces, mirror images of each other. Molds of three or more pieces may be necessary for the casting of complex forms, such as socketed axes. Some means must be furnished — like aligning lugs — to make the mold pieces fit together properly.

Molds usually are treated with a parting agent, usually powdered charcoal, which keeps the metal from sticking to the mold. Properly designed and used, an open or lidded mold or a split mold may be used many times. Many identical items can be made in this fashion before the mold needs to be replaced.

Casting in closed molds always leaves its mark on the product. Some metal leaks into the crack between adjoining parts and solidifies there. The casting freshly removed from the mold, has a thin projection of metal, called flash or fin, which is trimmed off in the process of finishing and polishing. If this line of protruding metal is not completely removed, it may be possible to detect the lines of juncture in the mold.

Casting by the lost wax (cire perdue) method was evidently an independent invention in each hemisphere. There are ethnographic records of the method in Europe, West Africa (by diffusion from Europe), and Indonesia. By implication of archeological artifacts the method was known in the Middle American area and in Peru.

In essence, the lost wax method involves the forming of a wax model of the object to be cast. Over the model layer upon layer of fine clay are placed until a mold is formed. In the forming process passages (sprues) must be left for the metal to be poured in and vents left for the gases. The model and its covering (the mold) are heated to melt out the wax. Then the molten metal is poured into the mold. Once it has cooled the mold is broken open and the casting removed. Major advantages of lost wax casting include the ease of formation of model and mold and the ability to make castings of complicated shapes; one disadvantage is the need to make a new model and mold for each item.

There are many variations possible within the general framework of lost wax casting. The model itself can be cast in order to make repeated castings of the same thing. Formed of several pieces of cast wax, the model can be assembled with yet other pieces of wax into a coherent whole. Any modeling materials which can be burned out of the mold can be used; some West Africans used insects and plants as their models.

When design considerations call for a bulky casting, such as the body of man or animal, then a hollow casting is desirable because its thinner wall will facilitate the escape of heat from the freshly-poured casting and conserve metal as well. A core is made which is the size and shape of the ultimate hollow. Over this is modeled a thin coating of wax to equal the thickness of cast metal. Pins of an unobtrusive metal are set into the core. They pass through the wax and protrude into the walls of the clay mold which is now formed over the wax. The whole mold is heated to drive off the wax, and the metal is poured. The mold is removed, the pins trimmed flush with the metal surface, the core broken out of the interior, and the casting polished. The entire process must be repeated with each article cast.

Though casting in split molds and other more refined methods are common today, lost wax casting remains the choice for works of art and for experimental, one-of-a-kind items.

Metalworkers' Tools

The forging tools of the metal worker were often quite simple. A stone anvil was commonly used because large pieces of suitable metal were not available or were too expensive to employ for such mundane purposes. If a metal anvil was needed for fine work the craftsman employed a "stake" — a small anvil, often resembling a railroad spike — which was stuck into a firm base (solid earth, a stump, a log) to hold it steady when in use.

Hammers, like anvils, often reflected the value and scarcity of metal.

Stone hammers were used for rough work and metal hammers for finer work; neither hammer was necessarily hafted. The metal hammer in East Africa, for example, was basically cylindrical and had one end worked to a point or to a chisel edge. It was grasped in the middle and struck on one end.

The anvils and hammers were often augmented with forms in stone and metal which served as swages. A special anvil might be grooved or have cavities into which the hot metal was hammered. A separate swage might be held atop the metal which in turn rested on the anvil. The top swage was then struck by the smith. Swages and similar forging forms were, of course, closely related to the products to be made. The ribs in many African spear heads were formed with the use of swages.

Chisels and punches were uniformly of metal because stone chisels, while adequate for woodworking, were not suitable with metal. Tongs were of the bent-loop type rather than hinged and if made of green wood rather than metal were adequate and cheap. In the absence of tongs green sticks were used; in fact, it was common practice in Africa to insert a part of the metal being forged into a green stick which then served as a handle until forging was completed. The same kinds of things which were used to handle hot metal were also employed to manipulate hot crucibles of molten metal or heated molds for casting.

Aside from the drawplate and any windlass employed, the only special tools for wire drawing were clamps to hold the wire. These clamps, of the loop type like common tongs, had a sliding ring on which the pulling force was exerted. Thus, the harder one pulled, the tighter the grip on the wire.

One of the first alien tools used by many primitive metal workers was the file, highly prized by these artisans. Not only did their use greatly facilitate the shaping and finishing of metal goods, but their metal was substantially harder and better than most nonliterates were able to make. Bits of wornout files can be found incorporated into many artifacts of the early contact period in different parts of the world.

Much of our knowledge about the metallurgy of nonliterate peoples has been systematically summarized from direct field observations of ethnographers, travelers, and others who have described techniques which have persisted into recent times (Cline, 1937; Wulff, 1966). However, another substantial body of data is of archeological derivation — from the metallurgical analyses of the products. These have been made for years and tell us something about techniques of manufacture, ore sources, sophistication of work as reflected in degree of consistency of product, and the diffusion of processes. Some archeological contexts have yielded the goods of the metallurgists themselves — their furnaces, crucibles, tools, and molds. The molds have occasionally been used experimentally thousands of years after origination, to cast further products of the original type, and thus to illuminate our understanding of these ancient technologies (Tylecote, 1962; Underwood, 1958; Rivet and Arsandaux, 1946; Forbes, 1950).

Social Organization of Metallurgists

It is difficult to characterize in a few words the social situation of metallurgists among nonliterate peoples, since simple smithing was something at which every householder may have tried his hand in some peasantries. However, more elaborate work was usually the province of specialist smiths; workers in precious metals were specialists regardless of other considerations; and smelters, because of the technical skill required, were usually full-time specialists.

Native Africa represents a full spectrum of social attitudes toward smiths and allied workers. In West Africa and the Congo smiths were held in high regard; some smithing families were, in fact, royalty who continued to practice their craft despite their social position. The king was expected to spend part of the day at his forge. However, West Africa and the Congo were areas in which almost all craftsmen were of good social standing. In the eastern parts of the continent, in present-day Kenya and Somalia, smiths were of very low social standing. In some tribes they were outcasts, pariahs, with whom no decent person associated freely; in fact, sometimes the smiths were not even a part of the tribes they served but were considered to be an alien people. By contrast with the west, eastern Africa was a region in which the few existing craft specialists of any kind were all unappreciated.

Because metallurgy was somewhat occult to many observers, its practitioners were often credited with extraordinary powers, not necessarily for the good, which were to be respected if not feared.

In general, whatever their social standing, smelters and smiths seem to have been socially distinct. They were recognizable as technical specialists and not simply practitioners of an intensified domestic craft. There was no developed domestic phase of true metallurgy which, setting a pattern of familiarity and experience, made of its followers mundane members of society.

15

Technological Change

Technological change does not differ markedly in character from cultural change, because technology is a part of culture. There are a few specific circumstances which influence the particular without affecting the general. These stem from the technical nature of technologies rather than from any exceptional factor which exempts them from consideration as parts of a culture.

Cultural change has been a focus of attention, but comparable interest has not been displayed in cultural persistence which is the other side of the same coin. The presumption is that persistence is the absence of change. The equation could be read as well in the other direction. Therefore, under the rubric of technological change we should consider equally the topic of technological persistence, for together they form an illuminating pair.

Some change-producing factors are: diffusion, innovation, and environmental change. These are named here in random order and any effort to assess their relative importance must be made within a specific context.

Diffusion, emphasized by several schools of theorists as *the* factor in cultural growth, means the transfer of cultural traits (units of behavior) from the members of one culture to those of another. Customarily we feel that such transfers of cultural materials include information on ways and means. The trait, details of its manufacture (if it is a material object), techniques for its employment, and some of the associated values may all be transmitted. The degree to which this is achieved varies widely from case to case.

Stimulus diffusion is a special class of intercultural transfer in which only the basic kernel of a trait is passed over. This then becomes the "stimulus" for development and elaboration on the part of its recipients. Instances of stimulus diffusion are difficult to establish because most of the criteria which are usually evaluated to make a case are lacking. The statement of stimulus becomes a statement of faith as much as of fact. A classic case of alleged stimulus is the development of plant cultivation in Southeast Asia from a stimulus presumed to have originated in the agricultural cultures of the Near East. The details of cultivation — the plants and the manner of their raising — are substantially different in the two areas. Only the essence of the idea, and some of its consequences, are the same.

An element in the occurrence of diffusion is the location of the societies in question. Groups which were geographically isolated, either in pockets within a large land mass or on the external margins, were not likely to receive much in diffusion. The ideas reached them late, if at all, and often in greatly attenuated form. The effects of location on diffusion are obvious in the debts owed to mainland cultures by the insular cultures of the British Isles and of Japan. While invasions were influential in the former case, no such explanation can be given for the Chinese influence in Japan.

Attitudinal isolation may be as effective as geographic isolation. A group may hold itself aloof from its neighbors, feeling that there is nothing worthwhile to be learned from such benighted people. Or the isolation may be that of complete satisfaction with one's own culture, to the point that no improvement can be imagined. And there were some societies, like the Shoshonean-speaking Indians of the Great Basin in western North America, who evidently were aware of the advantages in the practices of their neighbors but made no effort to change, for change involves effort and adjustment.

In this matter of attitudinal isolation, most societies evidently fall between the extremes — somewhat satisfied with life as it is but willing to change if the rewards seem great enough. This group probably profits most in the long run from diffusion because the traits they accept meet substantial needs and are not accepted simply for their novelty. The acceptance of new traits is infrequent enough to make possible a satisfactory integration or assimilation of these items without upsetting the direction of the culture which manages to maintain its identity and general character throughout. Societies which reject everything alien pass by the contributions of innovators elsewhere; they seem oblivious to the fact that no one society has a monopoly on the world's brains. On the other hand, those societies which accept every passing thing are likely to lose their bearings in the process; in the course of becoming everything, they become nothing.

Diffusion has engaged anthropologists who held simultaneous interests in technology and material culture; some of these students of diffusion are Henry Balfour (1893), Otis T. Mason (1895), Roland B. Dixon (1928), and R. U. Sayce (1933). The concept itself has diffused to allied social sciences and has led to research outside of anthropology. A fine survey of recent work and views is found in Everett M. Rogers's book (1962).

Innovation is a second source of change. The term was used by H. G. Barnett (1953) to replace "invention" and "discovery," terms he considered too difficult to differentiate and define. Too often their definitions incorporated some evaluation of importance or some implication of the motivation of the principal. To distinguish them is of little value when the net effect is that of "something new." There are some strong parallels in this matter of novelty with that of diffusion. An item diffused is also "something new," but a difference lies in the different origination.

The psychology of invention (read "innovation") has interested writers for some time (Rossman, 1964; Hadamard, 1945), but they seem little closer to an understanding today than when their research began. Some of the circumstances leading to technological innovation have been suggested, but the investigator of this type of cultural change is still thwarted by his inability to deal scientifically with the insight and introspection of inventors.

Monotony is alleged to have produced some innovations as the craftsman, tired of the repetitious nature of his task, seeks ways in which to shorten it or relieve the tedium while achieving the same ends. Some new techniques and approaches have no merit except that they are different, but this in itself may produce the famous "Hawthorne effect" in which any change in the situation improved the output of industrial workers (National Research Council, 1941:Ch. 4). Other innovations which have measurable merit and may come in time to dominate the field can result from the craftsman's need to amuse himself by playing with his craft while still meeting his production goal. Such developments are not likely to occur in the simpler craft situation where the worker, very much his own master, may refuse a potentially monotonous task, may interrupt a prolonged task, or may terminate a disagreeable task. When technological pursuits become more organized the individual craftsman, even though he is self-employed, gets caught up in the drive of the situation and loses some of his freedom. If he wishes to retain customers, apprentices, or his standing in the community of workmen, he must go on.

Craftsmen's display of virtuosity may lead to innovations. Craftsmen work not only for the consuming public but also to earn each other's approbation. A technical feat which gains the praise of the public is not necessarily impressive to fellow craftsmen. Therefore, at certain levels within a craft there are concerns and techniques which are esoteric, confined to the in-group. Though these serve a purpose in such a status, the innovations may rise to the level of public consciousness and public acceptance. They have, so to speak, proved themselves in the wider context and become a part of the acknowledged modus operandi of the field.

Once a new trait has arisen it must be accepted and integrated into the culture. The indigenous, innovated trait has an advantage over the diffused one: it is more likely to be in harmony with the patterns of the culture. The innovator, himself a practitioner of the culture, unwittingly will adhere to the standards and values to which he has been raised. The result is that he seldom will violate those standards and make his product unacceptable to his fellows. Thus it is probable that the new domestic trait will become integrated more rapidly than an alien one would.

If an innovation fails to be accepted in its own culture, it is likely to be lost until reinnovated. If, however, a trait in diffusion is rejected, it still exists elsewhere and may be offered again at a later date. The trait's life, if one may reify it, is not seriously affected either way.

Environmental change also predisposes to cultural change, but not by providing the material as in diffusion and innovation; rather, it provides the stimulus or motivation. It is considered separately from, perhaps coordinately with, the others, because of its importance in technological history. The traits which differentiate the Mesolithic cultures of Europe from their Paleolithic forebears are thought due to the close of the Pleistocene Epoch and the beginning of the Holocene. Increasing dessication of the Near East is considered one of the reasons for the rise of the Neolithic type of economy (Flannery, 1965; Wright, 1968). These were changes thrust upon peoples who remained in one place; other changes come to those who leave their accustomed habitat for another clime. Faced with immediate problems of survival, the usual response is to adopt a system from a group already acclimated. Diffusion is activated rather than innovation which is far too slow in so pressing a situation.

For millenia the changes in technologies proceeded at a pace similar to that of other cultural changes. There were no special pressures for technological changes and no special rewards when they occurred. The general evenness of development tended to keep cultures and their societies reasonably well coordinated. No one segment of either took great strides without time for the other segments to adjust; that is, there was no occurrence of culture lag (i.e., marked developmental disconformity between aspects of culture).

In the past several centuries a technological imperialism has developed to supplement the established economic imperialism of colonial systems. Emphases upon the development of markets and raw materials have been joined by insistence on the overhaul of native production systems: hand potters must yield to the wheel; the basket must give way before the plastic bucket; and stone masonry is supplanted by reinforced concrete. Such modern products and systems are to be valued for themselves as symbols of modernity, if not for their economic benefits.

At one time the people were allowed to choose for themselves what diffused traits or what innovations they would accept. Not all peoples, however, place values in the same order or on the same things. Westerners tend to stress the high value of technologies and readily accept changes in this aspect of culture, rewarding innovators, and equating change with progress or improvement. At the same time, changes in the social, political, or religious systems are viewed more cautiously as areas in which change is not equated with progress. Other peoples see their universe in a rather different light, placing technology and material culture close to the bottom of their priorities. (For a broad view of differences see Jean Herbert's (1965) text on Asian cultures.)

The world-wide pressure for modernization of technology in the Western European style has culminated in induced technological and social change in an effort to bring the underdeveloped ("developing," "have-not," "backward," and so forth) peoples into modern social and political life. The argument in many cases runs as follows. A heightened standard of living (itself measured in housing, hygiene, food, consumption goods) would bring democracy as more people had more things and there was less concentration of wealth in the hands of a few. It would relieve population pressure because it would soon be seen that only a few children need be born when nearly one hundred percent of them survive. Couples would discover that with no increase in wage-earners, larger families could not live as well as smaller ones. Experience has demonstrated that these sequelae, if they followed at all, were neither automatic nor prompt.

Technological change was acknowledged to be more than a problem for technologists. Social scientists were engaged to coordinate social, economic, and political changes with technological ones. Apparently, one kind of change called for yet another, so the team of change agents was augmented by experts of another stripe, and the dimensions of the effort were altered accordingly. Reflections of this involvement of social science are to be found in the writings of Spicer (1952), Mead (1955), and Foster (1962). It still looms large in the work of applied cultural/social anthropologists (Foster, 1969) and has led in the direction of developing interests in the nature of non-Western economies (Dalton, 1967; Bohannan and Dalton, 1965:1–32; Nash, 1966).

Despite difficulties, the efforts to accomplish these goals have intensified since World War II and have presented some interesting questions. For example, there is the question of historic recapitulation. If technologies of any sort are the end product of development upon development and experience upon experience, then is it possible to step in at the ultimate stage in this sequence and make it work? Do the technical personnel lack the insight bred of long experience? Some change agents are impelled by such considerations to insist on prolonged apprenticeship or basic training for their students before allowing them free rein. It is tantamount to asking for the reinvention of the steam engine before introducing railways. Though experience counts in the individual, he inherits none of the experiences of preceding generations except those which have become embedded in transmissible cultural practices which he can learn from alien instructors as well as from his fellows. In the final analysis, then, this counts for little.

There is the problem of choices and values. Under some circumstances it may be more feasible economically for a developing country to intensify its present activities than to engage in new ones. With the credits generated by known techniques, the country can import goods rather than manufacture them, if each group of technicians performs its specialized role and shipping costs are not excessive. Such an arrangement might be true, for example, of motor truck manufacture. The country is dependent upon outside markets for its goods and upon outside producers for an essential import. Regardless of the monetary merits of the situation, this solution may do nothing for the nationalistic spirit of the country when, perhaps, the nation's needs at this juncture are psychological and cannot be dictated solely by economic measures which exclude this element of cost. If there were not some factual basis in this argument for extra-economic values, there would be no justification for the production of anything save by the largest, most efficient, and most centralized of units.

Another problem hinges on the appropriateness of the solution. Technologies and technological solutions are a product of their cultural situation and are fitted to the particular problems confronting a society. Because they worked in western Europe is no guarantee that they will be applicable to the Bolivian Altiplano or in the oases of southern Morocco. In fact, circumstances may call for some entirely new behavior or entirely new application of an established one.

An illustration of a new approach and its consequences may be found in efforts to introduce solar cookers (Figure 58) into semiarid areas where

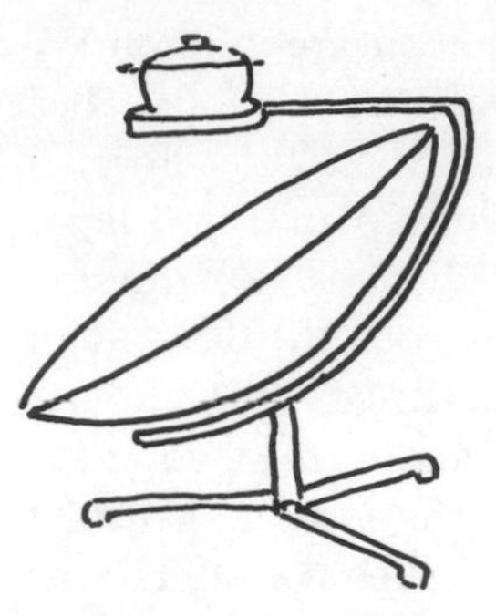

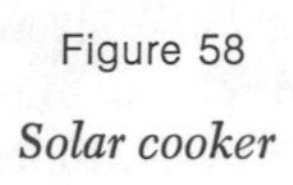

Figure 58
Solar cooker

fuel is scarce, but where there are many days of sunshine throughout the year. Consider, though, the limitations on the sun's "free" energy as captured by solar stoves which heat one pot at a time, only between ten in the morning and four in the afternoon. The pot or the stove must be adjusted at least every twenty minutes to keep it in focus and still the heat generated is equal only to one modest-sized burner of an electric stove. This device would function very well in a household which could be fed a meal prepared in one small pot in the middle of the day by a cook who did not mind the noonday heat and had nothing else to do besides tend the stove (Daniels and Duffie, 1955:66).

Even a new approach is fraught with difficulties, as the solar cooker instance shows. The overall integration of culture assures that much more will be entailed in successful induced technological change than the simple provision of information to the technically deprived.

16

Summary

This brief survey of the technological activities of nonliterate and pre-industrial peoples is intended to provide a sample of the many technological practices known from peoples the world over. It offers a perspective through time insofar as the information is available. Though the practices cited were not chosen in a random fashion, this survey makes an effort to be representative, not exhaustive.

There exists to date no technological study which encompasses the potential universe. Some studies consider in detail one place at one time (e.g., Clark, 1952); others cover a substantial spectrum, such as *A History of Technology* which is directed toward Europe and the Mediterranean basin (Singer, 1954); and still others deal exhaustively with technology in a smaller area, such as Needham's *Science and Civilization in China* (1954). The absence of the universal compendium is due to at least two factors: first, the necessary detailed data for individual cultures is not available; and second, the monumental task would dwarf most encyclopedias.

Man shares some aspects of his being with nonhuman primates who display elaborations of social relations, social organization, and communicative systems of some sophistication; however, man's habit of surrounding himself with a material world primarily of his own creation makes him very different from other primates and other mammals.

The possession of technology is reflected in man's physical evolution. The technological products — a shield between man and his natural environment — create an artificial (or cultural) environment in which man dwells. It would be inaccurate to say that this artificial environment suspends the laws of natural selection. However, it does immerse man so thoroughly in another context that he fails to perceive clearly the stringencies of this new environment to which he must adapt. By enabling some variants to survive which in the natural environment might prove disadvantageous, maladaptive, or lethal, culture broadens the range of variability of the species and may possibly foster speciation itself. (It may have done so in the past for all we presently know.) We do not know the direction of the new evolution, but we are sure that it exists and that human capabilities in technology are playing a part in its outcome.

The possession of technology is reflected in man's global distribution. The Primate Order to which man belongs is primarily a low latitude animal group, though some nonhuman primates have adapted to cold temperate climates. (At one time it was common to say that the order was tropical, but recent work shows a semiarid equatorial habitat for early forms.) Thanks to his ability to travel and to adapt, man has been found since prehistoric times in virtually every corner of the world except Antarctica. Though men have been able to make a direct physical adaptation to an astonishing range of habitats, from the fourteen thousand foot elevations of the Andes to the damp cold of Tierra del Fuego, in most instances adaptation has been assisted greatly by cultural practices.

The possession of technology has been closely linked with man's cultural evolution. Without accepting all of White's formulations, it is agreed that much of culture and society depends on the state of the technology. Man's exploitative capacities underlie the particular nature of population density and distribution, the closeness or looseness of the social bond, the relation of man to the supernatural world, and the span of the political structure. No one exploitative technique causes a given social consequence, but it certainly may make it possible by offering some opportunities and precluding others. As Mesthene has put it, "Technology alters the mix of choices" (1968:135). An interacting system of relationships exists between technology and the socio-cultural order, so that when one changes the other must respond.

The technological situation is not composed solely of techniques, materials, and tools. It also includes people, not all of them craftsmen, and ideas. Therefore, to describe and analyze this technological context one must integrate concepts from social anthropology, comparative religion, individual and social psychology, as well as technology.

Beyond the obvious technical content, each technological context includes the organization of craftsmen who may be members of a kin group or aliens, solitary workers or united into companies or guilds, persons of one sex and restricted ages or broadly representative of the working population. All must be related in some fashion to each other and to the population whom they serve.

The ideological aspect of technology — the values and attitudes a society expresses toward its material culture and its producers — is seldom explored in studies of technology. A case in point is the attitude of Americans toward automobiles, which are valued for other than the obvious pragmatic function of transportation. We know surprisingly little about parallel situations, especially in other cultures.

The writer hopes to have achieved two goals in the course of this volume. The first is to revive interest in the anthropological study of technology and material culture. Though some studies are dull, unimaginative, myopic, and guilty of generalizing from the particular, if handled imaginatively analyses of technology can be as interesting as those in any area of anthropological concern. They may also contribute as much to the development of anthropological theory as do studies of social structures, economic activities, or religious practices.

The second goal, with the nonanthropologist primarily in mind, is to induce in the reader an appreciation for the technological achievements of nonliterate, preindustrial peoples. Without the refinements of modern technologies these peoples produced workable practices which carried man along for hundreds of thousands of years to the threshold of industrialization. The interrelation and cumulation of item upon item and sequel upon antecedent has built a line of technological growth from the culture of earliest man, or perhaps before, to the present — a continuity which makes it imperative that anyone interested in today's technologies should know something of yesterday's.

Bibliography

ASCHER, ROBERT

1961 Experimental archaeology. American Anthropologist 63:783–815.

BALFOUR, HENRY

1893 The evolution of decorative art. London, Rivington, Percival.

1908 The fire piston. *In* Smithsonian Institution Report for 1907.

BARNETT, H. G.

1953 Innovation: The basis of cultural change. New York: McGraw-Hill.

BOHANNAN, PAUL AND GEORGE DALTON (EDS.)

1965 Markets in Africa. Garden City, N.Y., Doubleday.

BREUIL, HENRI

1949 Beyond the bounds of history. London, P. R. Gawthorn.

CHAPELLE, HOWARD I.

1957 Report to the government of Turkey on fishing boats. Rome, United Nations, Food and Agriculture Organization Report 706.

CLARK, J. G. D.

1952 Prehistoric Europe, the economic basis. New York, Philosophical Library.

CLIFTON, JAMES A.

1969 Personal communication.

CLINE, WALTER

1937 Mining and metallurgy in Negro Africa. Menasha, General Series in Anthropology 5.

COLTON, HAROLD S.

1939 The reducing atmosphere and oxidizing atmosphere in prehistoric Southwestern ceramics. American Antiquity 4:224–231.

DALTON, GEORGE (ED.)

1967 Tribal and peasant economies. Garden City, N.Y., Natural History Press.

DANIELS, FARRINGTON AND JOHN A. DUFFIE (EDS.)

1955 Solar energy research. Madison, University of Wisconsin Press.

DARK, PHILIP J. C.

1954 Bush Negro art. London, Alec Tiranti.

DART, R. A.

1957 The osteodontokeratic culture of Australopithecus prometheus. Pretoria, Transvaal Museum Memoir, 10.

DIXON, ROLAND B.
1928 The building of cultures. New York, Charles Scribner's Sons.

FLANNERY, KENT V.
1965 The ecology of early food production in Mesopotamia. Science 147:1247–1256.

FORBES, R. J.
1950 Metallurgy in antiquity. Leiden, E. J. Brill.

FOSTER, GEORGE M.
1948 Some implications of modern Mexican mold-made pottery. Southwestern Journal of Anthropology 4:356–370.
1962 Traditional cultures: And the impact of technological change. New York, Harper and Brothers.
1969 Applied anthropology. Boston, Little, Brown.

HADAMARD, JACQUES
1945 The psychology of invention in the mathematical field. New York, Dover (reprint 1954).

HANDY, E. S. CRAIGHILL
1923 The native culture in the Marquesas. Honolulu, The B. P. Bishop Museum Bulletin 9.

HARRISON, H. S.
1930 Opportunism and the factors of invention. American Anthropologist 32:106–125.

HERBERT, JEAN
1965 An introduction to Asia. New York, Oxford University Press.

HERSKOVITS, MELVILLE J.
1952 Economic anthropology. New York, Alfred A. Knopf.

HOLMES, W. H.
1919 Handbook of aboriginal American antiquities, Part I: Introduction: The lithic industries. Washington, D.C., Bureau of American Ethnology Bulletin 60.

HOMMEL, RUDOLF P.
1937 China at work. New York, John Day.

IVERSEN, JOHANNES
1956 Forest clearance in the Stone Age. Scientific American 194(3):36–41.

KELLER, CHARLES M.
1966 The development of edge damage patterns on stone tools. Man 1:501–511.

KROEBER, A. L.
1925 Handbook of the Indians of California. Washington, D.C., Bureau of American Ethnology Bulletin 78.
1948 Anthropology. 2nd ed. New York, Harcourt, Brace.

LINTON, RALPH

1936 The study of man. New York, Appleton-Century.

LOWIE, ROBERT H.

1940 An introduction to cultural anthropology. 2nd Ed. New York, Farrar and Rinehart.

MARTIN, PAUL S., GEORGE I. QUIMBY, AND DONALD COLLIER

1947 Indians before Columbus. Chicago, University of Chicago Press.

MASON, OTIS T.

1895 The origins of invention. Cambridge, The M.I.T. Press (reprint 1966).

1904 Aboriginal American basketry: Studies in a textile art without machinery. *In* U.S. National Museum Report for 1902.

MEAD, MARGARET

1955 Cultural patterns and technical change. New York, The New American Library.

MESTHENE, EMMANUEL G.

1968 How technology will shape the future. Science 161:135–143.

MOVIUS, HALLAM L., JR.

1950 A wooden spear of third interglacial age from lower Saxony. Southwestern Journal of Anthropology 6:139–142.

NASH, MANNING

1966 Primitive and peasant economic systems. San Francisco, Chandler.

NATIONAL RESEARCH COUNCIL, COMMITTEE ON WORK IN INDUSTRY

1941 Fatigue of workers: Its relation to industrial production. New York.

NEEDHAM, JOSEPH

1954 Science and civilization in China. 4 vols. Cambridge, Cambridge University Press.

NELSON, N. C.

1931 Flint working by Ishi. *In* Source book in anthropology. A. L. Kroeber and T. T. Waterman, Eds. 2nd Ed. New York, Harcourt, Brace.

OAKLEY, KENNETH P.

1950 Man the tool-maker. 2nd Ed. London, British Museum (Natural History).

O'NEALE, LILA M.

1932 Yurok-Karok basket weavers. Berkeley, University of California, Publications in American Archaeology and Ethnology, vol. 32, no. 1.

POPE, SAXTON T.

1923 Bows and arrows. Berkeley, University of California Press (reprint 1962).

RACHLIN, CAROL K.

1955 The rubber mold technic for the study of textile impressed pottery. American Antiquity 20:394–396.

Rivet, P. and H. Arsandaux
1946 La métallurgie en Amérique précolombienne. Paris, Université de Paris, Travaux et Mémoires de l'Institut d'Ethnologie 39.

Rogers, Everett M.
1962 Diffusion of innovations. New York, Free Press of Glencoe.

Rossman, Joseph
1964 Industrial creativity: The psychology of the inventor. 3rd ed. New Hyde Park, N.Y., University Books.

Sahlins, Marshall D.
1958 Social stratification in Polynesia. Seattle, University of Washington Press.

Salzman, Louis F.
1923 English industries of the Middle Ages. 2nd Ed. Oxford, Clarendon Press.

Sayce, R. U.
1933 Primitive arts and crafts. New York, Biblo and Tannen (reprint 1963).

Semenov, S. A.
1957 Prehistoric technology. London, Cory, Adams and Mackay (translation from Russian 1964).

Singer, Charles and others, eds.
1954 A history of technology. 5 vols. New York, Oxford University Press.

Sonnenfeld, J.
1962 Interpreting the function of primitive implements. American Antiquity 28:56–65.

Spicer, Edward H.
1952 Human problems in technological change. New York, Russell Sage Foundation.

Steensberg, Axel
1943 Ancient harvesting implements. Copenhagen, Nationalmuseets Skrifter, Arkoelogisk-Historisk Roekke 1.

Tylecote, R. F.
1962 Metallurgy in archaeology. London, Edward Arnold.

Underwood, Leon
1958 Bronze Age technology in western Asia and northern Europe: Part I. Man 58:13.

Wertime, Theodore A.
1964 Man's first encounters with metallurgy. Science 146:1257–1267.

White, Leslie A.
1949 The science of culture. New York, Grove (reprint 1958)
1959 The evolution of culture. New York, McGraw-Hill.

WILLEY, GORDON R.
1955 The prehistoric civilizations of nuclear America. American Anthropologist 57:571–593.

WRIGHT, H. E., JR.
1968 Natural environment of early food production north of Mesopotamia. Science 161:334–339.

WULFF, HANS E.
1966 The traditional crafts of Persia. Cambridge, The M.I.T. Press.

Supplementary Sources

Adair, John

1946 The Navajo and Pueblo silversmiths. Norman, University of Oklahoma Press.

Amsden, Charles A.

1949 Navaho weaving, its technic and history. Albuquerque, University of New Mexico Press.

Bailey, Flora L.

1940 Navaho foods and cooking methods. American Anthropologist 42:270–290.

Balfet, Hélène

1957 Basketry: A proposed classification. Translated and with preface by M. A. Baumhoff. *In* University of California, Archaeological Survey, Reports 37.

Boas, Franz

1927 Primitive art. New York, Dover (reprint 1955).

Bridenbaugh, Carl

1950 The colonial craftsman. New York, New York University Press.

British Museum

1910 Handbook to the ethnological collections. London.

Buschan, Georg

1922 Illustrierte Völkerkunde. 2 vols. Stuttgart, Strecker und Schröder.

Clark, R.

1935 The flint-knapping industry at Brandon. Antiquity 9:38.

Cooper, John M.

1938 Snares, deadfalls, and other traps of the northern Algonquians and northern Athapaskans. Washington, Catholic University of America, Anthropological Series 5.

Curwen, E. Cecil and Gudmund Hatt

1953 Plough and pasture. New York, Henry Schuman.

Digby, Adrian

1938 The machines of primitive people. Man 38:50.

Forbes, R. J.

1958 Man the maker. New York, Abelard-Schuman.

1968 The conquest of nature: Technology and its consequences. New York, Frederick A. Praeger.

FOSTER, GEORGE M.
1955 Contemporary pottery techniques in southern and central Mexico. New Orleans, Tulane University, Middle American Research Institute, Publication 22.
1956 Pottery making in Bengal. Southwestern Journal of Anthropology 12:395–405.
1959a The Coyotepec *Molde* and some associated problems of the potter's wheel. Southwestern Journal of Anthropology 15:53–63.
1959b The potter's wheel: An analysis of idea and artifact in invention. Southwestern Journal of Anthropology 15:99–119.

FUSSELL, G. E.
1952 The farmers tools 1500–1900. London, Andrew Melrose.

GOODMAN, W. L.
1964 The history of woodworking tools. London, G. Bell and Sons.

HEIZER, ROBERT F.
1966 Ancient heavy transport, methods and achievements. Science 153:821–830.

HERSKOVITS, M. J.
1954 Motivation and culture-pattern in technological change. International Social Science Bulletin 6(3):3–15.

HEWES, GORDON
1955 World distribution of certain postural habits. American Anthropologist 57:231–244.
1957 The anthropology of posture. Scientific American 196(2):122–132.

HINDLE, BROOKE
1966 Technology in early America. Chapel Hill, University of North Carolina Press.

HODGES, HENRY
1964 Artifacts, an introduction to early materials and technology. London, John Baker.

JONES, P. D'A. AND E. N. SIMONS
1961 Story of the saw. Manchester, Newman Neame.

KENT, KATE PECK
1957 The cultivation and weaving of cotton in the prehistoric southwestern United States. Philadelphia, American Philosophical Society, Transactions, vol. 47, pt. 3.

KRAMER, FRITZ L.
1966 Breaking ground: Notes on the distributions of some simple tillage tools. Sacramento, Sacramento Anthropological Society, Paper 5.

LAUFER, BERTHOLD
1915 The Eskimo screw as a culture-historical problem. American Anthropologist 17:396–406.

LIPS, JULIUS
1927 Fallensysteme der Naturvölker. Ethnologica 3:123–283.

LUCAS, A.
1948 Ancient Egyptian materials and industries. 3rd ed. London, Edward Arnold.

MACLEISH, KENNETH
1940 Notes on Hopi belt-weaving of Moenkopi. American Anthropologist 42:291–310.

MATSON, FREDERICK, ED.
1965 Ceramics and man. New York, Viking Fund Publications in Anthropology, 41.

MERCER, HENRY C.
1960 Ancient carpenter's tools. 3rd Ed. Doylestown, The Bucks County Historical Society.

MEWHINNEY, HUBERT
1957 A manual for Neanderthals. Austin, University of Texas Press.

MORSE, EDWARD S.
1886 Japanese homes and their surroundings. New York, Dover (reprint 1961).

O'NEALE, LILA M.
1945 Textiles of highland Guatemala. Washington, Carnegie Institution of Washington, Publication 567.

SHEPARD, ANNA O.
1956 Ceramics for the archaeologist. Washington, Carnegie Institution of Washington, Publication 609.

SLOANE, ERIC
1964 A museum of early American tools. New York, Wilfred Funk.

SMITH, CYRIL STANLEY
1965 Materials and the development of civilization and science. Science 148:908–917.

1968 Matter versus materials: A historical view. Science 162:637–644.

SOCIETY FOR THE HISTORY OF TECHNOLOGY
1959 Technology and Culture. vol. 1– , Cleveland.

SOCIETY OF CHEMICAL INDUSTRY IN BASLE
1937 CIBA Review. vol. 1– , Basle.

SONNENFELD, J.
1960 Changes in an Eskimo hunting technology, an introduction to implement geography. Annals of the Association of American Geographers 50:172–186.

SUNG YING-HSING
1637 T'ien-Kung K'ai-Wu: Chinese technology in the seventeenth cen-

tury. Translated by E-Tu Zen Sun and Shiou-Chuan Sun. University Park, Pennsylvania State University Press (reprint 1966).

THOMPSON, RAYMOND H.

1958 Modern Yucatecan Maya pottery making. Salt Lake City, Society for American Archaeology, Memoir 15.

TSCHOPIK, HARRY, JR.

1938 Taboo as a possible factor involved in the obsolescence of Navaho pottery and basketry. American Anthropologist 40:257–262.

1940 Navaho basketry: A study in cultural change. American Anthropologist 42:444–462.

1941 Navaho pottery making. Cambridge, Peabody Museum Papers, vol. 17, no. 1.

USHER, ABBOTT PAYSON

1954 A history of mechanical inventions. 2nd ed. Boston, Beacon Press (reprint 1959).

WHITE, K. D.

1967 Agricultural implements of the Roman World. Cambridge, Cambridge University Press.

WHITE, LYNN, JR.

1962 Medieval technology and social change. Oxford, The Clarendon Press.

WILDUNG, FRANK H.

1957 Woodworking tools at Shelburne Museum. Shelburne, The Shelburne Museum, Pamphlet 3.

Index

BCDEFGHIJ— H —76543